Kids SPEAK 5

Children Talk About Themselves

chaim walder

translated by Yocheved Lavon

FELDHEIM PUBLISHERS
JERUSALEM NEW YORK

Originally published in Hebrew as
Yeladim Mesaprim al Atzmam (Vol. 5)

First published 2006
ISBN 1-58330-912-8

Illustrated by Ruth Gavrielov

Edited, designed and typeset
by Eden Chachamtzedek

FELDHEIM PUBLISHERS
POB 43163/ Jerusalem, Israel

208 Airport Executive Park
Nanuet, NY 10954

www.feldheim.com

10 9 8 7 6 5 4 3 2 1

Printed in Israel

To my dear
children
for they are
the story of
my life

Tzviki
Moishe
Dudi
Noa
Tovi
Tali

Contents

Introduction

SIX YEARS HAVE passed since the fourth volume of *Kids Speak* was published. During those years, I've published other books — for kids, for teenagers, and for adults — including *Our Heroes, People Speak, Subject to Change, Behind the Mask*, and more.

I thought that four volumes of *Kids Speak* was enough, and that the kids would want something different. But it seems I was mistaken.

Over these past six years, thousands of letters have piled up on my desk, from children here in Eretz Yisrael and all around the world. In all those letters were stories — stories from kids who wanted their chance to speak.

And so, I decided to go on with the *Kids Speak* series.

In this fifth volume of *Kids Speak*, I focus mostly on subjects that bother kids in their everyday lives — problems with friends, fears, and difficulties in and out of the classroom.

The first and main story is about road safety. "The Zehavi Club" has also been produced as a play, and it was quite successful.

I would like to thank all the kids who took the trouble

to send letters to *Kids Speak*, P.O.B. 211, **Bnei Brak, Israel** during the past six years and before, although only a small number of their stories could be included in this book. The rest will have to wait patiently for future volumes.

*   *   *

And now, a few words to parents:

Various experiences of mine, as an educational counselor and therapist for children and teenagers at the Family and Child Center, find expression in this book and undoubtedly increase its value as an aid to children in coping with life's challenges.

I hope that these stories, which have passed the meticulous critical review of a panel of educators, will achieve their purpose and further the goal we all hold dear: molding and educating our children to the best of their potential.

Chaim Walder
Sivan 5766
June 2006

The Zehavi Club

My name is Ruthi.

I live in Jerusalem, on Shmuel HaNavi Street.

Have you ever been here? If you have, you know it's a very busy street. All day long, cars, trucks, and buses pass through, and sometimes they go so fast that it's really dangerous.

And it's not just the speed. It's also the smoke. There is so much pollution in the air from all the exhaust fumes that it's really unhealthy to walk around here and, even more so, to live here.

One time, my mother called to me to come out to the front balcony to take a look at the outside of our windows. They were black!

With a rubber squeegee, she scraped off the soot into a plastic bucket. There was a lot of it — a black, oily powder. "I just cleaned these windows a week ago," she said, "but the exhaust fumes from the cars have turned them all black again already. Think of it, Ruthi. This stuff in is the air we breathe. The amount you see here is the amount every one of us breathes in a week — Abba and I, and you, and all the rest of us!"

I started to cough just from looking at the soot in the bucket.

"But that's the least of our problems," my mother went on. "The soot is nothing compared to the danger we're in every time we cross the street. Just look at that car down there. That driver must be crazy!"

Someone driving a Subaru snaked his way in between two buses, passed a jeep that had stopped at a pedestrians' crossing, and almost hit two girls who were crossing at the crosswalk, the way they're supposed to.

"Did you see that?" said my mother. "That happens almost every half-hour. It's a miracle that those two girls weren't injured. I'm warning you, Ruthi: Don't cross that street without Mirel the Crossing Lady."

"But Ima," I protested loudly, "you know that Mirel the Crossing Lady is a kidnaper! I'm scared of her!"

*　　　*　　　*

Mirel the Crossing Lady. That's the more polite name for her. Some of the kids call her Mirel the Crazy Lady, or just Crazy Mirel. I have to admit, she's weird. She wears funny clothes, and every morning and afternoon she stands at the crosswalk, offering to help the boys and girls cross the street. Most of the kids try to avoid her, because she has another name besides Mirel the Crossing Lady: Mirel the Kidnaper.

She got that name because she keeps trying to make friends with all the kids, even if they don't want to make friends with her.

She's always asking them where they live, when they were born, and who their parents are. Usually the kids just run away without answering her.

At first, no one even knew where Mirel the Crossing Lady lived. All we knew was that she wasn't from our neighborhood.

But once, some kids followed her, and they found out that she gets on a bus to Holon every day. Everyone agrees that there's something strange and suspicious about a woman who comes all the way from Holon to Jerusalem every day just to help kids cross a street.

Michael the grocer likes to tell his customers about the day he first saw her.

"She got off a bus," I heard him say once, "and she started running like crazy, running all over the neighborhood as if she was looking for something. People jumped out of her way when they saw her coming. She ran in and out of buildings, looking at the names on the doors and ringing people's doorbells. People were scared; they thought she was dangerous, and they called the police. The police came and took her away in their van. But the whole neighborhood could hear her yelling. She was screaming, 'I'll find her! I'll come here every day, and you'll see — I'll find her in the end, and I'll take her away with me!' And ever since then, she's been coming here every day, looking for someone, just like she said. They've called the police many times."

There *is* something scary about Mirel the Crossing Lady. I think it's mainly her eyes. She has burning, green eyes, and she has a very strange way of looking at the children. Drivers who refuse to stop get scared, too, when she looks at them, and the way she yells would terrify anyone.

A lot of people in our neighborhood are worried about having Mirel the Crossing Lady around, and the kids have spread a lot of rumors about her. They say that she's a robber and that she's been in prison; and they say that sometimes she takes a little girl away with her and the girl's parents never see her again. They say all kinds of things about her. But Mirel the Crossing Lady continues to come here to help kids cross the street, and on their way across she asks them all sorts of questions.

When Mirel the Crossing Lady saw that the kids didn't really want to let her help them cross the street, she started working by a different method. Now, she doesn't take kids by the hand anymore; she stands in the middle of the road and stops the traffic so that all the kids crowded on the sidewalk can cross.

This method of Mirel's causes a big ruckus in the street every day. No driver likes it when someone stands in the road and blocks his way, and especially drivers who have no manners — drivers who won't even stop for a little girl who has been standing at the crossing for what seems like forever, pleading with her eyes that they should stop and let her cross the street.

Most of these drivers just grumble under their breaths, but some of them start honking their horns or yelling at Mirel the Crossing Lady, and then the street turns into a circus. Mirel doesn't care if she blocks the road for fifteen minutes — as long as the police don't come, she doesn't move.

She stands there and makes speeches in various different languages, all about those terrible drivers who endanger the lives of children. People get out of their cars and try to convince her to get out of the way, but they might as well be talking to a brick wall.

When Mirel isn't yelling at the drivers, she's yelling at the kids who don't wait for her to stop the traffic for them, but who just go ahead and cross on their own. There are a lot of kids like that — and I'm one of them. Sometimes it scares us when she yells, and sometimes it makes us laugh — usually both.

*   *   *

I've been begging my parents for the longest time to move to a different neighborhood. I can never get used to having thousands of cars passing under my window, and walking on a narrow sidewalk with them zooming by just a couple of feet away from me. They don't care if I'm trying to sleep, or even whether I have decent air to breathe. They don't seem to think my family and I have any rights at all — for example, the right to cross the street and reach the other side alive and well, without being scared out of our wits by reckless drivers that might run us over any second — and that has happened to at least a dozen people in the last few years.

Didn't little Yanky, who was killed the moment he stepped into the road, have a right to more than seven years of life? I know he shouldn't have tried to cross there, he should have gone to the crosswalk, but it's terrible anyway. And then there was Dvori. She lost her life, too, when she came out from behind a parked car, and the driver was going fast and couldn't stop in time. And what about Yoni? He was riding his bike in the street at night, and the truck driver didn't see him until it was too late.

I often think that living on this street has made me much sadder than a kid is supposed to be. Most kids don't have to see people getting seriously injured so often — and certainly not killed. May all you kids out there never find out how it feels to have a boy or girl you know get badly hurt — or, *chas v'shalom*, die.

But on the other hand, I've learned something that many kids don't know, and that is, how to look out for myself and be careful. At least I know how dangerous the street is, and I know I have to watch where I'm going and look both ways. Kids who live in smaller, quieter towns don't always realize how important it is to know all the safety rules about crossing streets — and to follow them!

It's not only kids who live in quiet places who don't know how dangerous the road is. Even the kids who live in the buildings across from us, on the other side of the street, didn't know.

Why is that? Because we, the kids who live on my side, have to cross the street every day, to go to school or to go shopping in the center of town, and those kids only have to cross if they want to come over here, to our buildings — so we have more experience than they do, and it shows.

When they would cross the street, you could see how careless they were. They would run out into the road from behind parked trucks, and that's really dangerous. If they were playing with a ball and it rolled out into the street, they would run after it. They wouldn't go to the crosswalk; they would cross the street wherever they happened to be. And they wouldn't always remember to look left, right, and left again before they crossed.

But all of that has changed now.

*   *   *

One day I was standing at the curb with some of my friends, waiting patiently for one of the drivers to kindly do us the big favor of letting us cross.

We stood there for about ten minutes, and then

some girls came out of a building on the other side of the street. Without stopping to think, they stepped right out into the road. Some cars that were heading towards them came screeching to a halt, and the girls crossed the street, laughing and saying to us, "What a bunch of scaredy-cats!"

We were too shocked by what had just happened to move, so we didn't take advantage of the chance to cross when the cars stopped for those girls. We just stood there, blushing, while they laughed and made fun of us. "You're such scaredy-cats, you'd stand there all day even if the street was empty!" one of them said. "You're afraid of getting run over by an electric pole!"

"That's better than being reckless!" I answered.

"Oh, you're just scared," she said again.

"You're just reckless!"

That was how it got started. From then on, there were two "enemy" groups of girls on our street, with each group calling the other group names. When I think about it now, I realize that we were all being very silly and petty, but at the time we were too busy fighting to see that.

The name-calling led to a very dangerous situation, because the girls in the "reckless gang" wanted to show how brave they were and to show us up. So they started taking all sorts of risks every time they crossed the street. They would step off the curb and walk right out in front of oncoming traffic, hoping the cars would stop for them. Sometimes the drivers would slam on their brakes, and other times they would just speed by, barely missing the girls.

My mother would sometimes see this from the front porch and say, "I smell disaster" — and she has a very good sense of smell.

I bothered me a lot, so I hung up a handwritten sign on the bulletin board in the entrance to the girls' apartment building that said:

Parents!
Your children are in danger!
Please teach them to be careful crossing the street.

But within an hour, someone tore it down.

Two hours later, a sign appeared in our building. It said:

The Scaredy-Cat Gang is hereby requested to stop bothering us with their warnings. We will cross the street when, where, and how we choose!

So, after a while, we stopped saying anything to them, because we saw that it only made things worse. The more we tried to get them to be careful, the more reckless they became. My father told me that just as it is a mitzvah to say something to people who will listen, it is also a mitzvah *not* to say something to people who won't listen. So we went on being careful, and they went on laughing at us — and taking terrible risks.

Of course, Mirel the Crossing Lady noticed their antics. She would yell at them, in her usual way, but they just answered her with chutzpah and insults.

*   *   *

One day, this state of affairs came to a sudden and tragic end.

Esther, one of the girls in the Reckless Gang, was crossing the street — as usual, without waiting for the cars to stop. What she didn't know was that her little sister Zehavi, seeing how easily Esther got across, decided to try the technique herself. She was standing at the crosswalk, waiting. A car was coming, and Zehavi stepped out into the road slowly, expecting the driver to see her and stop.

But the driver was going fast, and he must have

thought Zehavi would wait, and not cross until after he passed. He didn't slow down when he reached the crossing. It was only when he saw that the little girl was crossing right in front of him that he tried to slam on his brakes — but it was too late.

The whole neighborhood heard the sound of the impact. Up and down the street, windows opened and people stuck their heads out. They all saw the same thing: Zehavi lying on the road, and a light-blue car speeding away.

The driver didn't get out of his car to check how badly Zehavi was hurt or to try to help her. He was a hit-and-run driver.

In a few minutes the whole neighborhood was down there, standing around Zehavi, who lay motionless on the pavement. Men from *Hatzolah* came quickly and started taking care of her. Everyone was tense. She'd been hit so hard that none of them thought she could possibly live. The *Hatzolah* volunteers looked very worried, too. Zehavi was put into the ambulance, and they drove away with the siren wailing. Little by little, the crowd broke up. The grownups went back to their business, and we girls stayed there on the sidewalk, crying.

It was only a matter of time before accusations began flying around. When there's fuel all around, it takes only a spark to set it aflame. Dina, who lives in my building, whispered the words, "Reckless Gang," to Tzippi, who lives across the street.

Pandemonium broke out.

"You should be ashamed of yourself!" said Tzippi angrily. "Are you trying to blame us for what happened?"

"No, I just happened to mention the name of your gang, that's all."

"What do we have to do with it? Next you'll be saying that Zehavi got run over because of us."

"That's right! You guessed it! It was because of you! It was totally because of you that Zehavi got run over!"

"How dare you say a thing like that?"

"How dare I, you ask? You're the ones who are so daring! You dared to run out into the road, you dared to cross the street outside of the crosswalk, and you dared to step into the street without bothering to look both ways. You dared, and you dared, and you dared! So now it's my turn to dare. And I'm going to say it: It's your fault. It is! And if you try to deny it, then look at this!"

Dina reached into her pocket and took out the paper that the Reckless Gang had hung up. It said:

The Scaredy-Cat Gang is hereby requested to stop
bothering us with their warnings. We will cross the
street when, where, and how we choose!

"There's the proof, in black and white," said
Dina. "And you know what?" she added, with venom
in her voice. "I think the police might be interested
in this paper, too."

There was a tense silence. We were all in shock
at hearing Dina talk this way. A few seconds
passed, and then we all started screaming at each
other at once, drawing the attention of all of the
neighbors. Many popped their heads out of their
windows again, afraid that some new tragedy had
occurred.

"You can't accuse us!"

"Oh, yes I can, just watch me..."

"You're glad she got run over..."

"No, I'm not, I just want to prevent it from happening again..."

"Don't lecture us!"

"We've stopped lecturing you, and look what's
happened!"

Who knows what the fighting would have led
to if another uproar hadn't interrupted us at just

that moment. Suddenly, another ambulance came along. We didn't know why. It stopped on the other side of the street, a little way down from where we were standing. We looked and saw another knot of people gathering. We crossed the street — carefully — and wormed our way to the center of the crowd. This time, it was Mirel the Crossing Lady attracting all the attention. She was lying on the floor at the bottom of the stairway leading into one of the buildings. She wasn't moving.

One of the ladies from the building was talking to the ambulance crew. "Mirel saw the accident with the little girl," she said, "and she started acting strange. She felt sick, so I gave her a drink of water and offered to call an ambulance, but she wouldn't let me. Then, all of sudden, she fainted."

The ambulance crew examined her, connected her to an IV tube, and then put her in the ambulance and took her to the hospital.

Dina threw a meaningful glance at Tzippi and said, "Maybe you should ask yourselves what made her faint. Do you think this just 'happened by chance,' too?"

And the battle of words started all over again. But we couldn't hear one another. Everyone had something to say, and everyone was screaming it.

Then we saw Esther coming. She was walking fast and crying out, "Stop it already!"

We were frightened and stopped fighting as quickly as we'd started. We stood there, paralyzed.

Esther had tears in her eyes. In a choked voice, she said, "My parents just called from the hospital. They said my sister Zehavi is fighting for her life. That means she might, *chas v'shalom*... Oh, I can't believe this is happening," and she broke down crying. Finally, when she calmed down a bit, she looked at us and said, "What are you doing?! You should be saying *Tehillim* now, not fighting. What if Zehavi dies? I'll never forgive myself as long as I live," she sobbed, as fresh tears began rolling down her cheeks.

We were ashamed of ourselves. We tried to comfort Esther, saying it wasn't her fault and that Zehavi would be all right. Esther went back to her house, hoping that her parents would call again — this time with good news. There was nothing more to say, so we all went home.

The next day, we heard that Zehavi was lying unconscious in the hospital, and that her condition was very serious.

Conditions on our street, too, were very bad. It was as if we were divided in half, separated by

a border of hate and hostility. We had stopped
fighting, but now, instead of shouting and trading
insults, we had a cold war going on. The opposing
groups didn't speak to each other at all. If one of
the girls did try to talk to someone from the other
group, the girls from her own group would glare at
her so fiercely that she gave up *that* idea very fast.

Esther was the only exception. We didn't expect
her to take sides, besides we all felt sorry for her,
and besides, she was our only source of information about Zehavi.

*   *   *

Time passed, and Zehavi was declared out of
danger. But the doctors said she would have to go
through a long recovery process.

She was transferred to a special hospital for
people with serious head injuries, Levinstein Hospital in Ra'anana.

One day, Chedva (one of the girls on our side)
suggested that we go and visit Zehavi in the hospital. We asked Esther if she could let us know when
we could pay her sister a visit. She said she would,
and the next day she told us what day and time we
could come.

On the appointed day, five of us girls took a bus

to Ra'anana. It was a sad place to be. All sorts of terribly injured people were there. We saw many sights we would have preferred not to see.

We were told to wait in the visitors' room. We didn't know what to talk about, so we listened to what the other people in the room were saying. They were all talking about how they, or their friends or family members, had gotten hurt.

There was a boy named Roni who had been riding in the family car with his father. His father had stopped suddenly, and Roni had been thrown through the windshield because he didn't have his seatbelt fastened.

A girl named Aviva had come out from behind a parked truck, and a motorcycle had sent her flying.

There was a man named Meir, too. He had been hit by a car while riding a bicycle without a reflector.

All these people had lost their good health in an instant. And now they were badly injured, and most of them would be disabled for the rest of their lives, having to depend on other people's kindness. It was all so sad that we started to wish that we hadn't come.

Suddenly, the door opened, and four girls came

out of the patients' ward. We knew them — they were from the other side of our street, and one of them was Esther, Zehavi's sister.

There we were, face to face. We didn't know what to say. Then Tzippi hissed at us, "What are you doing here? Do you want to give Zehavi one of your lectures? You'd better just turn around and go home!"

Esther tried to calm her down, but Tzippi was still sore from our last encounter, and she paid no attention to Esther. She kept on firing insults at us.

Dina, once again, was the one who spoke up. "With all due respect to you," she said sarcastically, "you aren't Zehavi's only friends. You have no exclusive rights here. Your only special status is that everything that happened to her is your fault. So get out of our way and let us go in and visit her."

Esther's three friends stood shoulder to shoulder like a wall. "You're not going in," one said.

"Oh, really?"

"Yes, really!"

I whispered to my friends, "There's a door over there, maybe it leads to the ward." I pointed to it with my eyes, and we made a dash for it.

And they ran after us.

We were all behaving very badly, but what can I tell you? That's how kids act sometimes. We ran down the corridor, with me in the lead. As we reached the door, one of the girls cried out, "Hurry up and open it, the Reckless Gang is after us."

I turned the door handle, gave a push, and all five of us burst through the doorway together. A second later, the other four girls burst in, too. Only when we were inside did we realize that we weren't in a hospital corridor anymore, but in one of the rooms.

A girl was lying on a hospital bed. As we slowly moved closer to her, we saw that she had a smooth, pretty face. She didn't look sick at all. Her big, wide eyes were open, but they had no expression in them. *She looks like a doll*, I thought.

Then the door opened behind us, and a familiar voice said, "Tzivi, look what Mommy brought you..." We turned to see who it was, and we almost fainted.

The mother of the girl was Mirel the Crossing Lady.

*　　　*　　　*

We stood there, all nine girls, looking at Mirel, and we didn't know what to do with ourselves.

"How did you know that my Tzivi was here in the hospital?" asked Mirel the Crossing Lady.

"We... w-we didn't know," I heard myself answering. "We... um, we just happened to come in here."

"Very interesting," said Mirel. "Nine girls from your neighborhood just happened to come right to this girl's room, and this girl's mother just happens to be the woman they call 'Crazy Mirel the Crossing Lady.'"

"Really," I pleaded, "we really did come in here by chance. We were trying to visit Zehavi, and the Reckl... I mean, the girls from the other side of the street were blocking our way, so we tried to take a shortcut, and we ended up here... and then..."

"Yes, I get the picture," said Mirel the Crossing Lady. "You decided to bring your battles here. Here, the saddest place in the world. A place where people lie in bed for years, not moving a muscle. A place where people are willing to promise never to do anything wrong for the rest of their lives, if only they'll get well. This is where you came to fight?!"

We all looked down at the floor, we were so ashamed. Mirel the Crossing Lady was absolutely right.

"Go and visit Zehavi now," she said. "Or go back to that terrible street and go on with your childish fighting. Wait for me there in the street, so you can laugh at me when I try to help you cross."

Some of the girls turned to go, but I felt that wasn't the right thing to do.

"We never knew you had a sick daughter," I told her. "We didn't even know you had a daughter. Tell us about her. What happened to her?"

Mirel looked at me. It was a long look. For years, no one had talked to her. If they said anything at all, it was something disrespectful. But I wasn't being disrespectful at all.

Several long moments went by, and Mirel just stood there looking at us, saying nothing. We could see she was trying to decide whether or not to tell us about herself and her daughter.

"I wasn't always 'Mirel the Crossing Lady,'" she said suddenly. "Twenty years ago, when I got married, I was a talented, successful young woman. I had good organizational abilities, and I had a good job and made good money. Two years after my wedding, I had my first daughter, Shira. That was the happiest day of my life. Then, two years later, Tzivi was born. We were a happy little family. My two daughters were the whole world to me.

"Then came the tragedy. One afternoon, Tzivi was playing ball out on the sidewalk. The ball bounced into the road, and she ran after it. My husband ran after her to bring her back, and a car hit them both.

"My husband died of his injuries, and Tzivi... well, you can see for yourselves what happened to her. Her body was hardly hurt at all. But her brain..." Mirel sighed deeply, "her brain doesn't respond. For fourteen years I've been coming here, watching my sweet daughter grow, and she doesn't even know it. I talk to her all the time, and every now and then I see something that looks like a little tear in her eye. And that gives me hope. Someday, maybe she'll come back to me....

"I was in such grief that I started neglecting my-self. I started acting like an insane person. I just wanted to escape from the terrible pain — and that was the only way I could find. I was so busy run-ning away from myself that I began to neglect Shira, too — the only one I had left who was healthy and whole. And one day, she was taken away from me. I didn't understand why. I missed her terribly, and I started looking for her. Then I was told that Shira had been put up for adoption, and I would never see her again.

"I started crying and carrying on, and screaming that they had to bring her back to me. I promised to stop my grieving and behave normally and be a good mother, but they told me it was too late.

"I went to the city welfare department, I ran from one office to another, trying to persuade them to give me my daughter back, trying to convince them I was all right now, but it was no use. I began to understand that I had nothing left. I had lost my entire world.

"One day, on my way home from one of the meetings about the adoption, I was on the bus, gazing out the window at the people walking in the street with their children. I wanted so much to be like them, and then, suddenly...

"I saw Shira.

"She was walking hand in hand with a woman. I was positive it was Shira. She was walking by on the sidewalk, right next to where the bus was passing, but she wasn't looking in my direction.

"I jumped up and called out, 'Driver, stop the bus!' But he just gave me a sideways glance and kept on driving. I screamed at him, 'Stop, I just saw my daughter out there!' My screaming scared him, and he stopped right away. I jumped off the bus and started running towards the spot where I'd seen Shira.

"But she wasn't there anymore.

"I started looking for her in the nearby apartment buildings, yards, and side streets, but I didn't find her.

"At night, I had dreams about Shira and Tzivi. I began to be afraid all the time, afraid that what had happened to Tzivi might happen to Shira, too. I would dream that she was crossing a street, and she forgot to look both ways, or that she crossed between two parked trucks and didn't see the car speeding towards her. I must have dreamed about every dangerous way of crossing the street that there is, and the worst part of it was that I always saw my daughter in the dream, doing these dangerous things; but I couldn't reach her, I couldn't even cry out to her to warn her.

"I would get out of bed and pray for her, because even if I didn't know where she was, Hashem knew, and I begged Him to watch over her and keep her from harm.

"I went on that way for months, and still I was anxious day and night. I decided to go back to the place where I'd seen Shira, to look for her and try to protect her from getting hurt.

"I went back to where I'd seen her — it was in your neighborhood — and I've been looking for her ever since. It's been twelve years now. All this time

I've been looking for information, for clues, trying to track her down. And most of all, I've been trying to make sure that every driver that comes through this neighborhood will be scared of the weird lady who stops traffic whenever they dare to drive too fast, or whenever they won't stop for the children waiting at the crosswalk.

"Up until now, you've thought of me as Mirel, the Crazy Crossing Lady — the weirdo who yells at all the drivers and at all the kids, and always warns everyone about how dangerous the road is. But I am also a victim — a victim of the terrible accident that killed my husband, turned my beautiful daughter into a vegetable, and took my other daughter away from me."

"But, Mirel," I heard myself saying, "how come you never told us this story before?"

"I never told you?" said Mirel. "I screamed this story at the top of my lungs. In my own way, I told it loud and clear, over and over again. But the kids in your neighborhood weren't listening. They just laughed and made fun of me. I can't blame them. After all, a child is a child, and why should kids listen to a weird lady who yells at them?"

We didn't know what to say. We just stood there crying. I looked over at Tzivi, and I thought I saw a big tear rolling down her cheek. But maybe it was just the tears in my own eyes.

There was something I knew we had to do. For awhile I'd been thinking that we should do it, and now I knew the time had come. "I think it's about time we stopped fighting," I said. "Look at all the troubles other people have. Look at the kids in this hospital. And here we are, fighting and hurting each other for no reason. We shouldn't have blamed you for what happened."

Then I added, "In the name of all the girls in my group, I apologize, and I'd like you to come with us to visit Zehavi."

The girls were too ashamed to say anything; they just nodded their heads. I could tell they were glad to put an end to all the fighting.

Quietly, we all went to Zehavi's room. She was awake, but her eyes were dull and expressionless. Her head had been injured, and the doctors didn't know if she was going to get well.

There was an awkward silence. We didn't know what to do.

After a few minutes some of the girls started whispering among themselves. I knew we couldn't have that going on. I went and stood at Zehavi's bedside and said to all the girls, "Zehavi can't talk right now, but she hears us. So let's include her in our conversation."

We started telling Zehavi about the efforts the police were making to find the driver whose car had hit her, and about the demands the parents were making to have the city install speed bumps on our street, and other news from the neighborhood. Her eyes started looking a little less glassy. We could tell she was listening to what we were saying.

Shoshi spoke up and said, "Don't you girls think we ought to get together and fight against what's happening on our street?"

"But what can we possibly do?" asked Suri.

"Plenty," said Shoshi. "We can make things change. We don't have to put up with people driving through our street like maniacs."

"But how?" asked Suri.

"I don't know yet," Shoshi admitted. "But I'm sure we can do it. If we put our heads together, we'll come up with ideas."

"I can give you a whole list of ideas," said Mirel the Crossing Lady. We all turned and looked at her, as she entered the room. Zehavi looked at her, too.

Without waiting for an answer, Mirel the Crossing Lady launched into her speech, detailing all the ways that accidents could be prevented on our street. By the time she was finished, we were all fired up with enthusiasm to put the plan into action.

"Why didn't you think of this before?" we asked her.

"I've thought of it many times," Mirel replied. "But you never wanted to listen to me. I was just a neighborhood laughingstock."

"Oh, Mirel, I'm so sorry. I really apologize," I said, and all the other girls apologized too.

Mirel looked very moved. Then she left the room, and I sat down next to Zehavi and told her Mirel's story — everything she had told us. Zehavi's eyes filled with tears.

"I have a suggestion," said Shoshi. "Let's abolish both of our groups and start a new one."

"What should we call it?" I asked.

"I think we should call it the Zehavi Club — for two reasons. One, because we're starting it here in Zehavi's room. And two, because Zehavi (זהבי) stands for 'zehirus b'drachim — road safety.'"

"I get it," said Dina. "Zayin and hei stand for zehirus, 'caution,' and the veis stands for b'drachim, 'in the roads.'"

"But what about the yud in Zehavi's name?" one of the girls asked.

"*Yud* is ten," said Shoshi. "It's the ten of us."

"But we're only nine," I pointed out.

"Did you forget about Mirel?" answered Shoshi.

We said goodbye to Zehavi and promised to come again with more news.

*   *   *

The minute she got home from the hospital Shoshi spent several hours thinking up slogans to promote road safety. Later, in the evening, she sat with her parents, writing up a list of grievances that we had about the situation in our neighborhood.

The next day, the neighborhood was buzzing like a beehive. A few of the residents formed a committee. They typed up an announcement asking everyone to come out and demonstrate, demanding that the city make our streets safer. They made a lot of copies, and the Zehavi Club distributed them, breaking up into pairs and handing them out door to door.

At two o'clock the following day, the road was blocked by hundreds of adults carrying signs that said things like, "We want speed bumps" and "Give us traffic lights." We girls went and handed out illustrated material for kids, explaining the rules of road safety.

The demonstration caused an enormous traffic jam. The police redirected traffic, and representatives from the city council came to find out what our demands were, and they promised to do something about the situation. (City council representatives are very good at promising things.)

One of the fathers, who was appointed to speak for the group, told the police that until speed bumps were installed to slow down traffic on our street, we would slow the traffic down ourselves.

The next day the commotion was even bigger, and finally the policemen had to tell the demonstrators to get out of the street. The people obeyed police orders and cleared the road, but one girl remained standing in the middle of the street.

"Hey, you! Get out of the street, young lady," a policeman ordered her.

But the girl just stood there.

Some policemen started moving towards her, but people started yelling, "She's autistic! She doesn't understand what you want from her!"

It was Baylie. She was born with a condition called autism. Autistic people aren't capable of responding to their surroundings the way normal people do.

One of the policemen cautiously went over to

her, and gently escorted her to the sidewalk.

Then, before anyone knew what was happening, Baylie got into one of the police vans, grabbed the microphone, and started saying strange things over the loudspeaker.

"M-543," she said. "M-664, M-54, M-654. Mizrachi 0968767. Levine 20984849. Shemtov 40958439. Markovsky 798574398. M-843. M-56..."

"Do you hear what she's saying?" one of the policemen said. "I'm in shock."

"There's nothing to be shocked about," one of the neighbors tried to explain. "Autistics live in their own world. They're always spouting all sorts of meaningless phrases."

"Those are no meaningless phrases," the policeman corrected him. "You don't realize what she's saying? She's rattling off the numbers of all the police vehicles that have been here today and yesterday, and the names and badge numbers of all the policemen. It's incredible. She remembers them all by heart."

"M-89," said Baylie. "Yosefov 4834387. M-7214. Schleicher 74373298."

"Yosefov — that's me," said the policeman. "Look at my badge number. She got it exactly right. The girl is a genius."

All of us were stunned. We all knew Baylie, the poor autistic girl; she was an inseparable part of our neighborhood. But we'd never known she had a special talent like that.

Baylie finished calling out all the names and numbers of the policemen and their vehicles, and the crowd on the street began to break up. One of the police officers decided to take Baylie home.

I walked home with a few friends who were going my way. I was quiet, because I was thinking hard.

"I have an idea," I suddenly announced. "Let's go to Baylie's house and ask her mother where Baylie was when Zehavi got hit by the car."

"What difference does it make where..." Shoshi began to say. Then she suddenly understood. "That's a terrific idea! If Baylie got a look at the car that hit Zehavi, she probably knows its license number!"

*   *   *

We went straight to Baylie's house. Her mother answered our knock. She looked surprised to see us. Baylie didn't usually have girls her age coming around to see her.

We told Baylie's mother, Mrs. Goldstein, what had happened out there on the street, and about our idea how Baylie might be able to help the police catch the hit-and-run driver.

"Yes, she does have an incredible memory," Mrs. Goldstein agreed. "Let's try asking her."

She led us into Baylie's room. Baylie was sitting on a chair, staring up at the ceiling.

"Some friends are here to see you, Baylie," her mother said. But Baylie didn't even look at us.

"Baylie," her mother asked gently, "do you know Zehavi?"

"Don't know."

"Do you know Esther?"

"Don't know."

"Do you know Shoshi?"

"Don't know."

"But she does know us," I protested.

"Be patient," said Baylie's mother. "She doesn't think the same way as you and I. It takes patience to communicate with her."

"Who has a ponytail?" she asked.

"Girls have ponytails. Shoshi has a ponytail. Nava has a ponytail. Ora has a ponytail. Little boys have ponytails. Duvi has a ponytail. Motti has a ponytail. Mimi has a ponytail. Dini..."

"Okay, Baylie," said her mother. "Does Zehavi have a ponytail?"

"Don't know."

I saw that it wasn't going to be so easy to get information from Baylie.

"Zehavi was down there in the street."

"The street is black. To make a street, workers come and spread gravel. Then they cover the gravel with tar. A steamroller comes and makes the road smooth."

"She read that in a book," Baylie's mother explained. "Everything she just said is a quote from that book.

"Cars, Baylie," she said.

"Cars. Automobiles. An automobile is a machine designed to transport people from one place to another."

"We're not getting anywhere," said Mrs Goldstein.

"Try mentioning a blue car," I suggested.

"Blue," said Baylie. "Blue is one of the three primary colors, along with red and yellow. When blue is mixed with red..."

This just wasn't working. To get anywhere with Baylie, you have to try to get inside her head and think the way she does. I walked out onto their balcony to take a look at the spot where the accident had taken place. I tried to imagine the scene from the point of view of a girl who doesn't understand what's happening around her, but sees everything very clearly. I tried to recall the accident in detail. We had to find something about the accident that wouldn't make Baylie think of a word from the encyclopedia. A feeling...like pain. Or maybe pity. Could an autistic girl feel pity? Did she have emotions? I wasn't sure.

I went back inside. The girls were still trying to encourage Baylie to remember the accident.

"A car makes it hurt?" I said.

"A blue car makes it hurt. It keeps going; it doesn't stop. A girl gets hit. Baylie hurts. A blue car hits the girl. It hurts Baylie. The blue car goes away fast. A sign on the car, on the back of the car. 70-756-32."

My heart started pounding with excitement. "70-756-32?" I said.

"On the blue car. The blue car that hits a girl."

"Write that number down, Shoshi! Thank you, Baylie!" I almost screamed, and gave her a hug. She sat like a wooden doll, staring straight ahead.

"A car makes it hurt. A blue car hits a girl. She falls down. It hurts Baylie."

We thanked Baylie and Mrs. Goldstein. Then we went to my house, called the traffic division of the police department, asked for Officer Yosefov, and reported the information we'd received from Baylie. Within a day, the driver who had hit Zehavi was caught.

For a week, the people of our neighborhood put pressure on the city authorities, and finally they installed speed bumps and traffic lights. Our street was completely transformed. The drivers were forced to slow down when they came into our area, and, thanks to the traffic lights, kids no longer had to stand at crosswalks and wait for the drivers to take pity on them.

*　　*　　*

So things were going very well. But one person was left out of the picture — Mirel the Crossing Lady.

Suddenly there was no need for her. She'd been replaced by a traffic light. At first, she would come around anyway; but gradually, she stopped coming.

Zehavi was still in the hospital. The doctors said she might have to stay for as long as six months. We went to visit her every week to see how she was coming along.

One day, we decided to go and visit Mirel the

Crossing Lady's daughter. We went looking for her room. At first we got lost, but finally we found the door to her room. We knocked softly and stepped inside.

A teenage girl was standing there. She was startled by our sudden entry, and gave a little cry of alarm.

But we went in and arranged ourselves around Tzivi's bed.

The girl who was there before us looked frightened. "Who are you?" she asked us.

"Just girls. Who are you?" we asked, tossing her question back at her.

"I... I'm..."

"You're what?"

"I'm... Tzivi is..."

"What is Tzivi?"

"Tzivi is my sister," the girl finally blurted out.

"You mean, you're Shira, Mirel the Cr... you're Mirel's daughter?"

"I, uh, I'm just trying to meet my sister, if you don't mind."

"Excuse me," I said, "I don't understand. I mean, where have you been all these years? Do you have any idea how hard your mother's been looking for you?"

"I turned eighteen two weeks ago," said the girl, ignoring my question. "I always knew I was adopted. I have a lot of anger inside about that. I'm angry with my mother for abandoning me. I didn't even want to look into my adoption files to find out who she is. But I wanted so much to find Tzivi..." The girl began to cry.

"For Tzivi's sake I asked to have the file opened," she said. She turned towards Tzivi, who lay motionless in the bed, and she started sobbing. "I've missed you so much, Tzivi, for all these years. I haven't forgotten you for a moment. As soon as I turned eighteen, I went to the adoption agency and told them I wanted to know just one thing — where is my sister? They told me you were here in the hospital, so I came here. And what did I find? A sister who doesn't know me, who can't understand who I am even when I explain it to her.

"I thought, even if my mother doesn't want me, maybe my sister will be happy to meet me. But you don't want me, either — you can't want me. You can't even hear me!" she cried.

We all had tears in our eyes. It hurt so much to see someone in such anguish. We couldn't look at each other; we just stared at the floor. But then something happened.

Tzivi hadn't made a sound, yet we all heard her as if she'd called our names out loud, and we all looked at her at once. She was moving her head this way and that, as if she were praying. Her eyes were wet with tears. We couldn't believe it. This was Tzivi, who hadn't moved in years. Tzivi, who hadn't shown a trace of emotion in years. At first she only moved her head, but then the energy seemed to spread down into her body, and she managed to sit up a little. She stretched her hands out towards Shira, signaling to her to come closer. Shaking, Shira came close to Tzivi and hugged her for a long time, and they both just cried.

After a few minutes, I touched Shira's shoulder gently and said, "There's something I have to tell you. I want you to know that your mother never abandoned you. Not at all. You were taken away from her against her will."

Shira turned around. Her eyes were flashing with anger. "That's not true," she said. "I saw her signature. She signed on the dotted line that she was giving me up for adoption. She didn't want me."

"Shira, you've got to believe me. Your mother was suffering very much. She was in a very bad emotional state after Tzivi got hurt. They made her sign that document; she hardly knew what she was doing. And she's been looking for you all these years. Believe me, Shira."

She looked at me with contempt and said, "Why should I believe you? What do you know about it, anyway?"

"I know more than you think, Shira," I said softly, and then we all sat around Tzivi's bed, and together, we told her the story we'd heard from Mirel the Crossing Lady. We told her how her mother had been looking for her frantically for twelve years. The only thing we left out was the part about the not-so-nice names we used to call her.

When we finished our story, Shira seemed very moved. "Thank you," she said. "Thank you for telling me this. You have no idea how relieved I am. All my life I've been feeling so hurt, so insulted, thinking my mother didn't want me. Now I'm feeling like I can't wait to see her."

Shira had barely finished her sentence when the door opened, and who was standing there but Mirel the Crossing Lady?

Mother and daughter were face to face at last.

And the Zehavi Club had achieved all its goals.

As Bold as a Lion

My name is David.

I'm thirteen years old, and I live in Ofakim.

You may have heard about me, actually, because my story was in the papers.

It happened on a hot summer day. It was one o'clock, and I was heading home after the morning session at the *talmud Torah* where I go to school. Usually, I walk home with my friends. But that day I was alone.

Why was I alone? Because I got into a fight with my friends. It was about something silly, really. But it was me against all of them and we got mad at each other, so I ended up walking home alone.

Today, I realize that it wasn't "by chance" that we got into a silly fight on that particular day. Nothing that happens in this world is by chance. But at the time, I was in a bad mood because of it, just like any kid would feel if all his friends got mad at him at once.

Since I was walking alone, I was pretty bored, and my eyes were wandering, looking for some interesting sight.

But there was nothing interesting to be seen. Just a quiet, dull street. There were hardly any people outside, because it was so hot that day. Even the stores were empty.

So I decided that I would look at the cars I was passing, to see what models they were.

I don't know what made me think of the idea. I've never been interested in cars. My brother Naftali, he's the one who likes cars. Show him any car, and he'll tell you its name right away, and the model number, too.

So there I was, checking out the cars to see what make and model they were, and like I said, it wasn't by chance. That idea had popped into my head for a reason.

I noticed a blue Fiat Punto. There was nothing special about it, but something made me go over and take a look through the windshield.

That's when I saw that the car wasn't empty. There was a baby in that car. He was about a year old, and he was sitting in a baby's car seat, asleep.

I started walking away. After a few steps, I suddenly stopped. *A baby?* I thought. *Alone? Left in a locked car on a hot day like this? That could be dangerous!*

I went back to take another look at the baby. He was sleeping quietly, but he looked very red. I remembered a terrible incident that I'd heard about once. A little girl had been forgotten in a car, and it got so hot in there that she died.

My heart started pounding.

I looked around, but there wasn't a soul on the street.

I ran to the nearest store and asked the owner if he knew whom the car belonged to. He shrugged and said he had no idea.

I ran back to the car. I took a good look at the baby. He was very red and sweaty. His whole body looked wet.

I started getting nervous. That baby was in danger, and only I was there help him.

But how?

I tried to open the car door. It was locked. I looked at the baby, knowing that it might be a matter of life and death. I felt like crying, but I knew this was no time for crying. I had to do something to save that baby.

45

There has to be some way to get him out of there, I said to myself.

Then I had an idea.

My idea came into my head straight from Heaven. It wasn't something I would ordinarily do. I was going to break the window.

To tell you the truth, I wasn't so sure about this idea. The owner of the car might get mad at me, even if I explained that I was trying to save the baby. He might even have me arrested for breaking his window. Maybe he had only gone away for five minutes. He might think I had a lot of nerve to interfere in his business and break into his car.

But my next thought was that I had to break that window no matter what would happen afterwards. And that was what I was going to do.

After all, I had been there for five minutes already myself, and whoever was driving that car had been very irresponsible to leave a baby like that. A baby shouldn't be left alone even for a minute. So the driver couldn't make any complaints against me.

And besides, I really didn't care if he yelled at me. I had to do what I had to do.

Now all that was left was to find a way to do it. How do you go about breaking a car window?

I guess there are kids from other neighborhoods who would have no problem with that, but I had been raised to be a good kid, and I had no experience in window-breaking.

I looked around for something to use as a tool. *Maybe an iron bar or something like that*, I thought. Then I spotted a big rock. *That should do it*, I said to myself.

I ran over, picked it up with both hands, and ran towards the car with it like a madman. I came at the window on the driver's side, as far away from the baby as possible, and boom!! I smashed the stone against it.

It didn't break.

I took a few steps back, took a deep breath and got up all my strength, and ran towards the window again. I slammed the stone down as hard as I could. Boom! The whole neighborhood must have heard it. But the window still didn't break.

I looked at the baby again. He wasn't moving. Any baby would have woken up from all the noise I was making, and he ought to be screaming by now. If he wasn't moving, he must really be in bad shape. There was no time to lose.

I ran to the other side of the street so I could build up more momentum, and I came running at that car like a maniac, holding the stone over my head. Crash!

The window shattered into thousands of pieces.

*　　　*　　　*

This time the noise was so loud that a lot of people came running towards me. They must have thought I was a thief. That's what I would have thought if I were in their shoes.

But I had no time to worry about what they thought. I reached in through the broken window, unlocked the door and opened it, and then I opened the back door.

I got into the car. It was horribly hot in there. I unbuckled the straps that were holding the baby prisoner in the car seat. He was boiling hot. I took him out of the car and shouted to the people who had come running, "Call an ambulance quick. This baby is dying!"

With the baby in my arms, I ran to the store I'd gone into before and asked the man to help me cool off the baby. He led me to a sink at the back of the store and turned the faucet on. Carefully, I started wetting the baby all over to cool him off.

The baby didn't wake up. He was unconscious. The storeowner and I checked and found he was

breathing, but just barely. He wanted to give the baby water to drink, but I told him that it would be dangerous, since the baby was unconscious and he might choke on the water. That was what I had once heard. (And that wasn't by chance, either.)

The ambulance arrived in a few minutes. The paramedics took charge of the baby. They didn't drive away; they put him in the ambulance and gave him treatment right there on the spot. They connected him to an IV drip to get fluids into his body, and they put an oxygen mask on his face so he could breathe better. They closed the door so that they could take care of the baby without being disturbed. All we could do was wait.

The man from the store said to me, "Look, you're bleeding."

I must've gotten cut by the broken glass. But I didn't care. The only thing I cared about was saving that baby.

That was when his father finally showed up. He was very frightened.

"What happened to my child?" he asked wildly.

Instead of answering, all the people started yelling at him. "You should be ashamed of yourself! How could you leave a baby alone like that? Where's your sense of responsibility?"

The father looked totally miserable. "I only left him for a few minutes. There was a line at the post office."

That made the people even angrier. "They ought to take your child away from you, and find someone else to raise him," someone said.

"You were extremely irresponsible," someone else added.

"You're right," said the father, with tears in his eyes. "But what's going on with my little boy? Is he all right?"

He ran over to the ambulance and started banging on it like a madman. People pulled him away, so that he wouldn't disturb the medical team at work.

Holding a piece of cloth to my injured wrist (the storeowner had given it to me to stop the bleeding), I went over to the ambulance.

Suddenly, the ambulance door opened.

"Don't worry," the paramedic said reassuringly, "the child has regained consciousness."

We all breathed a sigh of relief.

"But if he'd spent another five minutes in that car, I'm not sure we could have saved him," he added.

*   *   *

The baby's father started to cry. Everyone felt sorry for him and forgot how angry they were. They started patting him on the shoulder and saying, "It's going to be all right. You made a mistake, but a miracle happened. Hashem loves you."

A tall, heavyset man took him by the arm and led him over to me. "You should say thank you to this boy," he told him. "He's the one who broke the window and got your baby out of there. He was even injured doing it."

The father looked at me speechlessly, and then he gave me a big hug and said, "Thank you. May you be blessed your whole life long. You saved my son's life." He started crying again, and I shed a few tears, too. I had been under such stress, and now it was over.

Well, almost over. Next, the police came.

They took the father aside and told him that there would be a police investigation and they would probably bring charges against him. He told them to do whatever they wanted; he didn't care. He was just happy that his child had been saved.

He handed his driver's license over to them, and then got into the ambulance to accompany the baby to the hospital to be examined and put under a doctor's supervision.

The people crowded around the policemen. I couldn't hear what they were saying, but all of a sudden they all looked at me and said, "This is the boy."

One of the policemen came over to me, clapped me on the shoulder and said, "Good work, kid. You saved that baby's life. I see you're a bit injured, so I won't bother you now, but just leave us your name and address, because we're going to need you as a witness. And you'll probably get a certificate of commendation, too."

Then he added, "You know, you're a brave kid. A lot of people, if they came up against a situation like you were just in, would just stand around staring, or maybe yelling, or maybe they'd call us to come and do something. But you had the courage to act. I've seen very few people in this situation who had the courage to go ahead and break the window — and none of them was as young as you."

At last I could go home.

*　　*　　*

The story spread around town and even appeared in the newspapers. I was called in to testify in court, and I got a certificate of commendation from the police. That was nice, but for me, the most important thing was what the rabbi of our town said to me.

"You know," he said, "you have a certain very important quality. If you put this quality to good use, you could grow up to become a great leader of the Jewish people. The quality I'm talking about is called *tooshiyah*, which means 'resourcefulness.' But actually it is more than that, because not only does it mean being resourceful, it means having the courage to take action. A person with this quality," the rabbi explained, "knows how to do the right thing at the right time.

"Many people," he said, "know how to do something, but they don't have the courage to use their knowledge. Some people know how to sing, for example, but they're afraid to put their talent to use and sing in front of other people.

"Some people are good at learning, but they don't have the courage to teach others.

"Some scholars know the *halachah* very well, but they don't feel confident enough to act as a guide to others — to answer their questions and instruct them on what to do in a particular situation. In order to become a *rav*, a scholar needs to have the courage to be a leader.

"Even a wise person isn't always courageous

enough to give the right advice. He may know deep inside what the answer is, but he may not be brave enough to say it out loud.

"It says in *Mishlei* (28:1): '*Tzaddikim* are as bold as a lion.' You know, David, you too were as bold as a lion. You have proven that you have the courage to spring into action when need be. You saw a child in danger, you thought immediately of the correct course of action, and you were able to carry out that course of action," said the rabbi. "I have great hopes for you. Study the Torah well, put all your strength into it, and use that remarkable quality of resourcefulness that Hashem has given you, to become a great scholar and leader of the Jewish people."

*   *   *

That's my story. I didn't write it in order to brag or boast; I just want to encourage other kids, too, to have the courage to do the right thing at the right time. If you know that the idea in your head is the right thing to do, then don't leave it inside your head — put it into action!

Sometimes situations come up where you know what you have to do. For example, let's say a little kid has put something in his mouth and he starts choking on it. Many people may know what they're supposed to do in such a situation, but not everybody does it. Only someone with inner courage jumps in to do what has to be done; other people just start screaming, or they call an ambulance, and then they find out that they've called the fire department by mistake, and meanwhile....

Having *tooshiyah* also means saying the right thing, saving people from embarrassing moments, and never standing by helplessly.

If my story will make even one kid do the right thing in a tough spot, then it was worth writing it, just for that one boy or girl.

Holes in the Wall,
Wounds in the Heart

My name is Tova.

I live in Jerusalem; I'm in the seventh grade.

I'm an ordinary girl, a little on the quiet side. I'm kind of tall and thin.

I'd like to tell you about a hard time I went through with my circle of friends. For a while, I was staying in the classroom for recess instead of going out and joining in the games. I even stayed home for a week, because I didn't want to go to school.

Not that I was always that way. Up until that day — the day I'm going to tell you about — I was doing fine. I had plenty of friends. I got along with all the girls, and the teachers liked me.

But a few months ago, something happened. It was on a Monday. I stayed in the classroom for recess with three other girls, and we were playing games. Five other girls were there, just talking or whatever.

Suddenly, my friend Tami had an idea, and it sounded all right to the rest of us. She offered to teach us modern dance.

"You know how to teach modern dance?" I asked. "Where did you learn that?"

"Well, you know about my sister," she said. "She performed in that show a couple of weeks ago. She had a solo dance number. She loves it, and she's always doing it at home. I learned it by watching her. If you want, I'll teach it to you, too."

"Okay," I said. "Go ahead, let's see it."

To tell you the truth, we weren't that interested — it sounded about as much fun as a melted snowball — but we didn't want to hurt her feelings; she was so enthusiastic.

As soon as Tami started dancing, we saw how wrong we'd been. It was a very funny dance. When we saw the dance steps, we all began laughing hysterically.

It went something like this: two jumps forward, two jumps back, and kick the wall twice. It was more of a joke than a dance, really.

"You call that a dance?" I said to Tami, in between giggles.

I guess you'd have to see it to know how funny it really was. The more we laughed, the more excited Tami got, and the more power she put into those jumps and kicks.

Her next step, as you've probably guessed, was to invite us to join in. We didn't need much encouragement. It looked like so much fun that in a moment, we were all taking two jumps forward, two jumps back, and giving two sharp kicks to the wall.

Pretty soon a crowd of admirers had gathered around to watch — or at least we flattered ourselves into thinking that. Anyway, having an audience got Tami even more excited, and we followed her lead.

The next thing I knew, after my turn came to give two good kicks — right, left — to the wall, I found myself staring in shock at two big holes in the wall.

I guess you've figured out by now that it was a flimsy, plasterboard wall.

"Oh no!" said a voice. "What are they going to do to you now?" It was none other than Tami.

What followed was complete pandemonium, and I was pretty scared, wondering what all the girls were going to say, not to mention the teacher — and the principal.

At first, I thought I was in luck when I saw how all the other girls reacted. They got quite a "kick" out of those holes in the wall, and a few of them decided to do a repeat of my performance. What I'd done by accident, they were doing on purpose.

It wasn't long before there were a few more holes in the wall. They weren't as big as the ones I'd made, but I think it was a worse *aveirah* on their part, because I hadn't meant to do it, and they did it on purpose.

The bell rang, and we went back to our desks, tired and sweaty.

*   *   *

When the teacher came in, she didn't even notice the holes in the wall, until a few really "nice" girls made sure to draw her attention to them. I'm sure you know how that's done: you look towards the holes (or whatever it might be) and give a little gasp, and in a few seconds the teacher will be looking just where you want her to look.

It worked in this case, too. The teacher asked, "What's going on over there?" and a few smart alecks answered in unison, "Somebody made holes in the wall!"

As you'd expect, the teacher wasn't exactly too

pleased. She was very upset, and started talking about the sin of damaging property and what a serious *aveirah* that is. I knew she was right, but my feeling inside was that it wasn't my fault, because I hadn't meant to do any damage.

But my nightmare had only just begun.

Next, the teacher started looking for the culprit. "I want to know who did this," she said.

And then something happened that I wasn't expecting. Almost the entire class held up their hands and called out my name.

And when I say almost, I mean the whole class, except for two girls: myself and a girl named Efrat.

Efrat had never been in my circle of friends, and to me she was just another one of my classmates. She's a quiet girl, very intelligent and mature. She's tall, too. But despite all her good qualities, she doesn't lead the class in popularity. Oh, and I forgot to mention — she has a heart of gold. But I guess you can see that from the story, since she was the only one who didn't raise her hand and put the blame on me.

The teacher had a free hour in her schedule that day, and she asked me to come and have a talk with her. I could see it wasn't going to be a short talk, and I've always been afraid of talks with teachers — even if they're short. This was actually the first time I'd ever been called in for a talk with a teacher, and I was very scared. At the next recess I just didn't know what to do with myself. I was shaking from head to toe, and besides being scared, I felt very insulted by the way the whole class had taken a stand against me — even my friends, and even the girls who had made their own holes in the wall.

In our class, if a girl is called in for a talk with the teacher, her best friend is allowed to go with her. All of a sudden I found out that I didn't have any best friend, although until that moment I'd had a whole group of girls who were supposed to be good friends of mine.

Now, in case you're wondering why I didn't realize before this that I didn't have a best friend, it's because I'd never been called in to talk with a teacher before. I guess I never gave any thought to the question of whether I had a truly good friend or not. This was a moment of truth for me, and the truth wasn't very pleasant. Nobody was willing to go and take a scolding from the teacher together with me.

It was Efrat who volunteered to go with me to meet with the teacher.

I was glad to accept her offer, and together we headed for the teachers' room. I was shaking in my shoes all the way, and meanwhile Efrat tried to comfort me, reassuring me that she would be by my side for my "trial and sentencing."

There was no one in the teachers' room except our teacher. She invited us to be seated.

We sat down.

Efrat started talking, and I felt she was really saving me by doing that. She told the teacher the whole story. The teacher listened, asked a few questions, and got honest answers. Then there was a silent pause, and I was very scared, wondering what she was going to say. And then...

Then all she did was smile and say, "Well, I'm sure that next time it will be a case of 'look — and think — before you leap.'" And with the same smile she sent us back to the classroom.

Now I realized that my fear of the dreaded "talk with the teacher" had all been for nothing. She'd given us a chance to explain, and she accepted our explanation. It was so easy.

*   *   *

But I soon realized a few more things, as well. Things about my friends and classmates.

The next day, they all started giving me the third degree, asking me questions like, "What did the teacher say?" "Did you cry?" and "Did she yell at you?"

Efrat and I decided just to smile at these questions and say nothing. We felt that after they'd shown such disloyalty, they really didn't deserve a report on what had happened. But unfortunately, things got more complicated than that.

The new friendship between Efrat and me seemed to make the other girls jealous. First they tried a "divide and conquer" technique. They tried to get each of us alone and get the information out of us that way. But they didn't manage to divide us, or conquer us either. And then they decided to act.

Shevi, the queen of the class, who rules with an iron hand, started mobilizing her troops against me. "We'll take care of that snob," she told them. "We won't speak to her until she gives in."

They followed their orders. From that day on, nobody said a word to me, as if I were some kind of untouchable. I have to admit, it totally broke my heart.

That evening, one of the girls, Malka, dared to violate the ban. She called me on the phone to tell me what else Shevi was plotting against me.

Starting the next day, no one was to come near me, and if I touched something, no one else could touch it, as if I were contaminated or something. It sounded so weird; it got me all upset.

I got so scared of Shevi's plans that I didn't want to go to school for the next few days. But I didn't tell my parents what was going on, and that was a terrible mistake. Instead, I told them I didn't feel well, and I stayed home for two days. On the third day I knew I couldn't go on claiming that I was sick, and anyway they could see for themselves that my "symptoms" came from the fact that I wanted to stay at home.

Reluctantly, I went back to school. I'd decided to tell everyone that I was going to be transferred to the other class, and that really was what I'd intended to do. I thought that by doing that, I would get the girls to regret the way they'd been acting.

But instead, before I got there the girls in my class made sure to spread the word to the other class, about all the "terrible things" I'd done. They even conducted a "guided tour," inviting a bunch of them over to our classroom to see the damage with their own eyes. I was caught with nowhere to go. There was no place left for me in my class, and it was no use moving to the other class, either.

The situation was becoming totally unbearable. I started thinking more and more about changing schools.

I talked to my mother about it. I told her I wasn't happy in my class. But she absolutely vetoed the idea of changing schools. Even though she sympathized with what I was going through, she felt that I would be able to work things out. She wants us kids to learn to deal with our problems. Sometimes that's a good thing, but this time it made me feel terrible.

Things got worse every day. Those holes in the wall were a symbol of the wounds in my heart, which got deeper all the time. My classmates were hurting me so much that one day, after hours of insults and humiliation, I made up my mind that I wasn't going to school anymore. My mother saw how desperate I was, so she let me stay home. She thought it would only last a few days.

For a week I didn't go to school, and the only one who called me or showed any interest in how I was doing was Efrat. She tried to persuade me to come back to school, but I stubbornly insisted on staying home, until finally I got so bored roaming around the house all day that I decided to go back, no matter what was waiting for me there.

I walked to school with my eyes downcast and my heart full of dread. It may sound crazy, but I was scared to go to the school I'd been going to since first grade. I didn't know what kind of reception I was going to get from the girls. After all those years of friendship, they had turned into my enemies.

*   *   *

I reached the school building, and timidly made my way to my classroom. I went inside.

But then I got a surprise. All the girls talked to me normally, as if nothing had happened. Even Shevi, the one who had organized the anti-Tova movement, talked to me just like in the old days.

At first, I was suspicious. I thought they had another trick up their sleeves. But I watched carefully as I talked with them, and soon I saw that they really were treating me normally, as if nothing had ever happened. It seemed like a miracle; I couldn't figure it out.

At recess, Malka came over to talk to me. She was the one who had kept me informed of the plans the girls were making against me, and now she told me what had been going on during my absence.

The day before, during the morning roll-call, the

teacher noticed that I'd been absent for a almost a week, and she asked if anybody knew why I wasn't coming to school. No one said anything; and then Efrat, who hardly opens her mouth as a rule, stood up and told the teacher that I was at home, hurt and insulted because of the way my classmates had been treating me.

The teacher rebuked the class for their behavior. She said she happened to know that I wasn't the only one who'd made holes in the classroom wall, and that even if I had been the only one, it wasn't done intentionally, and that it was unjust for them to treat me that way.

This was an opportunity, the teacher said, for the girls to see how considerate the teachers are towards the girls. "Here's a perfect example of a girl being judged harshly by her classmates, and yet look at how the teaching staff handled the matter. I was angry about the holes in the wall, too," she admitted, "but it never entered my mind to hurt a poor girl who had done such a thing unintentionally — especially a girl who is generally well-behaved. It was you girls who made harsh judgments and hurt her so badly."

The teacher told the class about an experiment that was done in a certain place: they set up a school where the students were the ones to decide what the curriculum would be, who would teach them, and who should be punished.

"At first," said the teacher, "many children were jealous of the kids who went to that special school. They thought that nobody ever got punished there, and that the students could do whatever they wanted. But that wasn't the case. In fact, the students were harsher with their punishments than any teacher would have been. For a little mistake, a child could be expelled from the school, or get all sorts of other severe punishments. The teachers felt sorry for the kids, but they couldn't do anything about it, because according to the school rules, the students were in charge.

"To tell you the truth, I never really believed that story," the teacher went on. "I thought it was too far-fetched, and that children would never punish each other that way. But from my own class, I've learned that it isn't so far-fetched after all.

"Look at what happened here," said the teacher. "A girl was learning a dance. She got a little over-enthusiastic, maybe a little clumsy, and she ended up damaging the wall. I understood that as soon as I heard the explanation, so I wagged my finger at her a little, told her to be more careful in the future, and that was the end of it. But what did you girls do? You put her to shame, you organized a cruel ban against her, and you brought others in from the other class to embarrass her. Isn't that proof of what I'm saying?

"This goes to show you that adults — parents and teachers, for example — can be more soft-hearted and considerate towards children than their classmates are. Because the adults were also children once, they understand that kids make mistakes sometimes and do things they shouldn't. That's why kids need to be taught how to behave, and sometimes even punished if that's the only way to teach them, but never in a way that will cause them harm.

"I'm afraid kids don't understand this very well. Sometimes they may think their teachers are just looking for somebody to punish. But when they're put in the judge's seat, they're much more severe and much less considerate than their teachers are. Not because they're evil, but because they lack experience."

The teacher's words had a strong effect on the class, and Malka told me that they were planning to ask me to come back, but I came back on my own before they had a chance.

All this happened a few months ago. I think the girls have forgotten the whole story by now. But I haven't forgotten.

I haven't forgotten how hurt I was, or how scared I was of being left without friends. I know now that my most serious mistake wasn't that I made holes in the classroom wall, but that I stayed home from school. That could have ruined my life — if I hadn't had such a good teacher.

Now I realize that every kid goes through tough experiences with his friends at some time in his life. There will always be a time when it seems as if he has no friends and that no one ever will be his friend.

But this isn't really true.

Difficult times come and go, yet they're forgotten after awhile; and when they're over you find out that these tough experiences help you to deal with life later on.

Now that this is over, I think I've gained from it, because I've learned a lot about life, about friends, and about myself.

But my biggest gain, however, was Efrat — my best friend.

That's right. Efrat is now my best friend. After the ordeal, I didn't forget how kind she'd been and how much loyalty she'd shown, and I decided that this was the girl I'd like to have as my closest friend.

I felt shy about telling her that, but one day I got up the courage to say it to her. And when I did, I thought I saw a little tear in her eye — it must have meant a lot to her to hear me say that. There was one in my eye, too.

Efrat said she felt the same way towards me, and now I think the whole thing was worthwhile just to get a good friend like her.

That's the story.

They've already fixed the holes in the wall of our classroom.

And as for the wounds in my heart, they're also almost healed now....

Scatterbrained

My name is Moishy.

I'm twelve years old. I'm a pretty good student, and I'm friendly with everyone.

But I have one problem: I'm a very disorganized kid. I lose things a lot. I may have something in my backpack today, but that doesn't mean I'll know where it is tomorrow.

My notebook covers and my Gemara always have "dog ears."

I pay a high price for being this way. You have no idea how it feels to lose a notebook that you've worked hard on for months, or to miss a class party because you forgot and then to hear about how great it was the next day.

But no matter what it costs me, I'm just not able to change. Warnings from my teachers don't help either, and neither do campaigns and prizes for not forgetting things. I'm still a disorganized, scatterbrained kid.

*   *   *

Last year, summer came early. It was very hot, and it was hard for us to concentrate in class. One of the boys came up with the idea of collecting money so we could buy fans for the classroom.

Our teacher offered to appoint three boys, one from each row, to collect $2.50 from every boy in his row, and when all the money was collected, we would buy a few fans.

It was a good idea, except for the choice of collectors. The chosen boys were Efrayim, Simcha, and me. That last choice wasn't such a good idea. Maybe I should have said something, but when the teacher said my name, I didn't stop to think how scatterbrained I was. I guess I forgot that, too...

I was happy to be chosen for the job, but an hour later, I'd already forgotten all about it.

When school was over, I saw Simcha going from seat to seat in his row, reminding all the boys to bring the money the next day, and then I remembered that I was supposed to be doing the same thing, so I did.

The next day, I collected a total of twenty dollars

from my row. Four boys forgot to bring the money (I guess I'm not the only forgetful one), and I told them not to forget to bring it in the next day.

At the end of the day, I went home, put the money in an envelope, and forgot about the whole thing.

The next day, the four boys who hadn't chipped in yet came over to me and gave me $2.50 each. That made ten dollars. I put the money in my backpack. After recess, the teacher asked us to give him the money we'd collected. Simcha gave him thirty dollars, Efrayim gave him thirty dollars, and I...

I was busy searching frantically in my backpack.

Finally I found the money. Only it wasn't the full amount. I had ten dollars there, the money I'd collected that morning. Where were the missing twenty dollars?

"Moshe, I'm waiting," I heard the teacher say.

I broke out in a cold sweat. "I'm looking for it," I said. "I'll find it in a moment."

But I didn't find it. Not in a moment, and not five minutes later, either. And those five minutes felt more like five hours. I felt like all the kids were staring at me (which was true), and there I was with only ten dollars.

"I'm sure the money's here in my backpack," I said. "It has to be here."

"I suggest that we wait until the next recess," said the teacher, "and then you can make a more thorough search."

He started the lesson, but I couldn't concentrate. All through the lesson I was rummaging through my backpack. I kept my eyes on the teacher, but my hands were under the desk, searching every compartment of that bag.

I opened every zipper and checked all the little inner pockets. I found a lot of interesting things, including things I'd lost about half a year ago, but I didn't find the one thing I was looking for. The money.

It was time for recess again. The teacher came over to me. I started emptying out my backpack. I was pretty embarrassed about all the strange stuff that was piling up on my desk.

When my bag was empty, I started looking on my shelf in the closet, but I didn't find any money there, either.

I told the teacher that I hadn't found the money, and that it must be somewhere in my house. My face was red, and I was sweating all over. I felt so dumb.

When I got home, I searched my room, or I should say, I searched through all the heaps of junk in my room. Once again, I found some lost treasures — missing notebooks, and all sorts of things I'd lost during the past few months. But one thing, I didn't find — the thing I was looking for.

*   *   *

Now I had no choice; I had to go and tell my father all about it. I told him I was in trouble, because I'd lost money that wasn't mine, and I had a responsibility towards the class.

My father just looked at me with raised eyebrows. I thought about what I'd just said: "I have a responsibility," and I realized why he did that.

"I know, Abba," I said miserably. "I'm irresponsible. I'm disorganized. I'm forgetful, and I'm scatterbrained." I started to cry.

My father waited for me to calm down, and then he said, "You're not the only one in the world who's forgetful and scatterbrained, Moishy. There are lots of people like you. But someone who cares about himself will take steps to remedy that trait.

"Your problem," he continued slowly, "is that you have a certain other trait, too, and if you are able to change that trait, you'll go a long way towards solving the problem of being scatterbrained."

"What trait do you mean?" I asked.

"Maybe this isn't the right time to tell you," he hesitated. "You're already upset, and I don't want to make you feel even worse."

"No, Abba — please tell me. I want you to help me solve my problem. It's making me so miserable."

"Did you straighten up your room a little while you were looking for the money?" he asked.

"A little," I said.

"And I bet you found things you lost months ago, right?"

"Yes, that's right."

"That should tell you something. It should tell you that the problem of forgetfulness can be solved through orderliness. But you hardly ever put your things in order, and that is because of yet another character trait."

"What character trait?"

"Laziness," said my father. "You don't put your things in order because you're too lazy, isn't that true?"

I nodded my head.

"But what am I going to do now?" I said, almost in tears. "I'm scatterbrained, I'm forgetful, I'm not orderly, and I'm lazy, too! And I owe my class twenty dollars, and if I don't bring it tomorrow, they're going to say that besides all those wonderful character traits we just mentioned, I'm a thief, too."

"All right, then, let's make a deal," he said. "You may have certain deficiencies, but you're still a good-hearted, studious, intelligent boy, and besides, I love you, and I don't want you to get into trouble with your class."

"So what's the deal?"

"So I'm going to take twenty dollars out of my wallet and give it to you, so that you can pay back the money you lost."

"Thank you, Abba," I said, "but I feel very bad that you should have to pay for the fan for my whole row in class."

"Don't worry, I'm not doing it for free," he answered, with a mischievous look in his eyes. "In return for these twenty dollars, I want you to put your room and your backpack in order every single day for the next twenty days. And when I say put your room in order, I mean your entire room: your bed, your clothes, your books, your notebooks, your shoes, your belts, your pencils and pens — absolutely *everything*."

"Okay, it's a deal," I said quickly. I knew I had no alternative. I had no other way of coming up with twenty dollars, and if that was the price I had to pay, I would pay it.

*   *   *

My father gave me the money, and the next day I came to class and gave it to my teacher. Luckily for me, he didn't ask any questions. I had a feeling, though, that he knew I hadn't found the lost money and that I'd brought these twenty dollars from home. Apparently, he decided not to say anything about that, but it was still pretty embarrassing.

When I got home, I started cleaning up my room. It was hard at first, but the more progress I made, the better it looked, and the better I felt.

The next day, I straightened up the room again. The main tasks were to fold the clothes and make my bed.

After a few days, it was taking me just a few minutes to straighten up each day, because the room was already clean and orderly, and all I had to do was keep it that way.

One day, my father came into the room, complimented me on what he saw, and said, "I'm sure it's much nicer for you to be in your room, now that you're keeping it so neat." He paused for a moment and then said, "How about taking it a step further and sort out your *sefarim* and books by size and subject? Let's try and get that just as orderly as the rest of the room. I don't like to see a *Chumash* next to a math book, and a Gemara next to an atlas..."

As soon as I heard the word "atlas," I jumped up. My father looked very surprised, but I knew what I was doing. I dashed over to the bookshelves, took down the atlas, opened it, and...

Out fell the envelope that contained the twenty dollars.

I'm so scatterbrained. When I collected the money that day, I was worried about where to put it for safekeeping, and I put it in the first place I thought of. At the time, I knew where I was putting the money, but a moment later, I'd already forgotten. And I didn't remember it again until I heard my father say the word "atlas."

Jumping for joy, I brought the money to my father. "Here," I said, "I'm paying you back the twenty dollars. I didn't lose a penny of it."

"Does this mean that our deal is off?" he asked.

I thought for a moment before I answered. "Yeah, it's off," I said. "Now I don't have any obligation to straighten up my room every day. Right, Abba?"

He looked surprised and upset, and he nodded his head in an uncomfortable way. I think he was a bit angry with me, but he had no choice. A deal is a deal.

"I won't straighten my room because I have to," I continued. "I'm going to straighten it every day because I want to. Because I'm not lazy, and I want to fight against being scatterbrained."

My father threw his arms around me and gave me a warm hug, then he mumbled something about me being a great kid, and left the room.

I'm not going to tell you that I stopped forgetting things from then on. I can only tell you that I've stopped being lazy, and that I'm fighting hard every day not to be scatterbrained.

And I think I'm getting better at it.

There's a Burglar in My House!

My name is Elisheva.

I'm thirteen, and I live in a small town.

Something strange happened to me about a year ago, and I'd like to tell you about it.

There are four kids in my family, and I'm the second. One day, my parents were away from home, about an hour's drive from the house. My big brother was in yeshivah, my younger brother had gone to visit our Zeidy, and my sister had gone to visit a friend in the city. Everyone was out of town except me, and I was lounging in my room, reading a book.

My room is tucked away in a corner of the house. You can't see it from the hall; you have to go into my sister's room in order to see that there's another room next to it.

Anyway, I was lying on my bed, reading, when suddenly I heard someone trying to open the front door. (It was locked, of course.) I was frightened for a second, but then I thought it must be my parents coming home. I waited to hear the sound of them putting their key in the door, but nothing happened.

I have a phone in my room, and wanted to call them on their cell phone, just to hear it ringing, because that would reassure me, but I didn't do it just then because I had music playing in the background, so I figured I wouldn't hear it ringing anyway.

Then I heard the window opening, and someone coming in! I thought it must be my younger brother, because no one else in the family would come in through the window.

I called up my Zeidy's house to see if he was there. Sure enough, my Zeidy called him to the phone. In the background I heard the sound of forks clinking against plates; they were in the middle of eating lunch.

"I think there's a burglar in the house!" I whispered. "I heard him come in!"

"Where are you?" he said.

"In my room."

"Go into my room and lock the door," he advised me. "Your room has no lock."

I told him I felt safer in my own room, because it was hidden, and I hung up.

Meanwhile, I heard someone moving things around. I imagined the burglar, emptying out the house. I heard the door open, and I figured he must be putting all our stuff into a van outside.

The phone rang and I answered very quickly so the burglar wouldn't hear it. It was my brother, he was worried and wanted to know what was happening. I told him that I heard someone moving things, and I hung up.

Then I took a cell phone, which I had right next to me, and called the police. "There's a burglar in my house, robbing us, and I'm here all alone!" I said. "Please come fast!"

At that very minute, the regular phone rang again. My brother had decided to call the house to see who would answer. As I picked up the receiver, someone else also picked up downstairs.

Whose voice did I hear answering the phone?

My younger sister's!

Speaking into the cell phone again, I told the police secretary, "Never mind, it's all right," and I hung up.

I was so tense. I burst into tears and was shaking for about fifteen minutes before I finally calmed down.

*   *   *

So what were all the sounds I was hearing, you want to know?

It turned out that my sister didn't go to visit her friend after all, because the people who were going to give her a ride weren't able to take her. She came home, thinking no one was in the house, because usually on that day of the week, there's no one home when she gets there.

My sister tried opening the front door, and of course it was locked. She looked in the hiding place where we keep a spare key, but it wasn't there. Then she remembered she had a key to the back door in her bag, so she went around to the back and unlocked it. That was the sound I heard like someone opening a window.

We usually don't use the back door, and there were some big jerry-cans there, blocking the way, so she had a hard time opening the door. She tried to push them out of the way. That was the sound I heard of somebody dragging things around in the house. She managed to squeeze her way in, and then she went and opened the front door from the inside so she could get her backpack, which she'd left outside. That was when I thought the burglar must be putting all our stuff into a van!

Then my brother called, and she and I picked up the phone at the same time.

So the mystery was solved.

I hope you'll publish this story in your book.

I'm sure that there are a lot of kids like me, who imagine all sorts of scary things when they hear noises.

Maybe this story will help them to understand that they shouldn't panic over every noise they hear — usually there's an explanation for these things. Real life is not as exciting as what we sometimes imagine.

Elevator to Panic

My name is Gadi.

I'm eleven years old and I live in Petach Tikvah.

My story began four years ago, but it went on for a long time after that.

You've probably heard of Ezer MiZion. It's an organization in Israel that helps sick people and their families. One of the things they do is run a sort of hotel where families who have sick children can stay while their kids are in the hospital, so that they can be near them and visit them a lot.

My story happened in one of these hotels, a place called Oranit.

Now you're probably thinking I was sick, and that I want to tell you a story about that. But, *baruch Hashem*, I wasn't sick, and no one in my family was sick, either. The reason I was at Oranit was to go to a party they were having there, a party for sick kids and their brothers and sisters (because if one of the kids in a family is very sick, the other kids suffer, too). There were going to be singers and clowns there, to entertain the kids and make them feel good.

So what was I doing there?

My father was one of the people who organized the party. I won't say any more than that, because then you might figure out who I am.

And now for the story:

During the party, a friend of mine came over to me (his father was also one of the organizers). "Let's go play with the elevator," he said.

"Okay," I answered, even though I knew that an elevator isn't really a toy that you play with, and even though my mother had warned me that kids under fourteen aren't allowed to ride in elevators alone.

So if I knew all that, why did I say yes?

Maybe because I once lived in a building with an elevator, and most of the kids in the building used it without having an adult with them, even though they were under fourteen. So I thought there was nothing really wrong with going and having a little fun.

*   *   *

We got into the elevator and starting riding up and down from the ground floor to the next floor and back again. We would get out and run back in again. Sometimes the doors would close before we got there, and then we would race down the stairs and catch the elevator on the ground floor again.

I admit it was a silly game, but at the time it seemed like a lot of fun.

We got in to ride upstairs for about the tenth time, and I didn't notice that we'd pushed the button for the second floor by mistake. Instead of going just one flight up, we went two flights up. The doors opened and I ran out. Suddenly I found myself in a dark hall. I tried to run back to the elevator, but the doors closed before I got there, and down it went.

When the elevator doors closed, I was in total darkness, because the only light in the hall came from the elevator. There I was, all alone in a dark, empty hall, and I didn't know my way around at all. And remember, I was only seven years old then.

I can't describe how terrified I was. At first I was afraid to move; I just stood there waiting for my eyes to get adjusted to the darkness. But it was pitch black and I couldn't see a thing. I decided to try and feel my way to the stairs. I knew they were to the left of the elevator.

Taking tiny steps and keeping a hand on the wall, I walked to the left. I came to a door, found the handle, and opened it.

But the door didn't lead to the staircase. It led out to a large balcony.

It looked as though there were no stairs leading to this floor. The only way to reach it was by elevator.

I went back to the elevator and pushed the call button. But the elevator didn't come. I guess the kids were playing with it downstairs.

I started to feel really scared. I was afraid I'd be stuck up here forever, and no one would know where I was. To tell you the truth, I can't remember what I was thinking exactly. I was too terrified.

Then I heard someone scream. A horrible, loud scream, and then another one. It took a few moments for me to realize that I was the one who was screaming. I screamed and screamed, and finally, the elevator came. The doors opened and a nice-looking man inside asked me what was wrong. I didn't answer. I just got into the elevator with him and rode down to the ground floor.

My parents were waiting there, very worried. They'd also heard me screaming, and they didn't know what had happened to me.

I started crying like I'd never cried in my life. My mother hugged me and asked me what happened, but I couldn't answer her. I just cried and cried.

After I calmed down a bit, I asked my parents to take me home. They said the party wasn't over yet, but I kept insisting I wanted to leave, so my mother took me home in a taxi, and my father stayed until the party was over.

On the way home, I told my mother how scared I'd been, and I started crying again. My mother told me not to worry, because all kids go through scary experiences sometimes. She said I should try to get over it now.

*   *   *

At first, I thought I had gotten over it, because I almost forgot all about it. But one day, I had to go to see a doctor. My mother and I went into the building where the doctor had his office, and what did I see there?

An elevator.

Suddenly, the whole thing came back to me. My legs started shaking, and I told my mother I wanted to go home.

"What's wrong?" she asked. "Do you feel sick?"

"The elevator," I said.

"You're afraid it's going to take you to some unwanted place again?" she laughed. "Don't worry, I'm with you."

I didn't know how to explain it to her, but I just couldn't get into that elevator. Logically, I knew I had no reason to be afraid, but the elevator reminded me of how terrified I'd been that other time. It brought all those feelings back to me. I couldn't even think about getting into that elevator.

So my mother and I ended up walking up four flights of stairs. I felt bad that my mother should have to walk, and I told her that maybe she should take the elevator and let me walk up by myself. But she said, "All I need is for you to be all alone in the staircase and get frightened, and then I'll never be able to take you anywhere again, unless it's on the ground floor."

She was right. I *was* scared to go up the stairs all alone. I was just being polite when I said she should take the elevator. I was glad she walked up with me, even though I was sorry to make her climb all those stairs.

Over the next few years, I hardly ever went into an elevator. I say "hardly" because there were a few times when I really had no choice, like one time when we stayed in a hotel, and our room was on the ninth floor. But I took an elevator only if I really had to, and when I did, I had butterflies in my stomach the whole time, even though my parents were right there with me.

Again and again, my father tried talking the problem over with me. He said there was no logical reason to be afraid of elevators, and that it's safer to ride in one than to cross the street, even on a green light. I agreed with him, but my fear was stronger than his logic.

A few months ago, during Sukkos, my father said we were going to a party. The party was being held at... Oranit. Right away, all my brothers and sisters looked at me.

"I'm not going," I said.

My father didn't answer.

When it came time to go to the party, my father told me I was coming along. "Tell me," he said. "Do you want to get rid of this elevator-phobia of yours?"

"Of course I do!" I said. "But it just won't go away."

"I have an idea to make it go away," my father said. "But in order to try out my idea, you have to come with us to Oranit."

That really scared me.

"Are you going to make me ride in the elevator?" I asked.

"I'm not going to force you. Come with us, and you'll see."

I was curious, so I agreed to go. But deep down I really went because I wanted to solve my problem once and for all.

*   *   *

As soon as we got to Oranit, I started to feel afraid. We went inside, and there was the elevator. My father said to me, "Now, how about coming in with me and showing me what floor you got to that day?"

"You'll go with me?"

"Yes, I'll go with you."

I was scared, but I went into the elevator. My father was right behind me, and he asked me to push the button for the top floor. I pushed it, and the elevator started going up.

I held my breath. (I always do when I have to take an elevator. It's no problem holding your breath for two flights, but just try doing it for seven flights, some time.)

The doors opened. There was that dark hallway again. We stepped out.

The doors closed, leaving us alone in the hallway. It was just like it had been four years before,
when I was seven and got stuck there, only this
time I was older and my father was with me.

"So this is where you stood four years ago,"
my father said. "And you didn't know what to do,
right?"

I nodded. Then I remembered that my father
couldn't see me nodding, because we were in the
dark, so I said, "Yes."

"Okay," he said, "now let's try and find a way
out of here."

"If we go to the left, we'll get to a balcony," I said.
I remembered the door I'd found that day, thinking
it led to the staircase, and how frightened I'd felt
when I saw nothing out there but the open sky.

He asked me to take him there. I started leading
him towards the door, and when we got there, my
father asked me to open it.

We went out onto the balcony. My father asked
me to look down and tell him what I saw. I saw the
street, the cars in the parking lot, the bus stop....

"Okay," he said, "let's go back inside."

We went back inside, and my father asked me to
lead him down the dark hall.

We started walking down the hall, very slowly.

I felt a lot of doors along the way. They were all locked. Finally we came to the end of the hall.

There was a door there, the same kind of door that led to the staircase on the other floors. I opened it.

There was the staircase, right before my eyes.

"Let's go downstairs," he said.

We walked down one flight, and then another flight, and in a moment we reached the ground floor.

We went back to the elevator.

My father looked at me. I was breathing hard.

"Now we're going to do the same thing a few more times," he told me.

I pushed the call button, and we took the elevator to the dark hall. We went to the door leading to the staircase, and walked down. Then we went back to the elevator.

"All right, let's do it again," he said.

We went through this routine at least five times. "How many more times do we have to do this?" I asked.

"I don't know," he said. "We'll keep doing it until you feel ready to do it by yourself."

"By myself? Alone?"

"Right," said my father. "Alone."

We walked down the stairs again, and went to the elevator.

"Come with me one more time," I said, "and then I'll try it by myself."

"I'll come with you as many times as you need," was his answer. "Even a hundred times, until you feel you know this building so well that you're not afraid anymore."

We rode up again, and walked down.

The next time, I got into the elevator by myself. I almost asked my father to come with me, but I decided I could do it. I pressed the button for the top floor.

The elevator took me up, the doors opened, and I stepped out. The doors closed, and there I was, all alone in the dark hall. Just like four years ago.

But I felt different. Completely different.

Not that I was calm, exactly. I felt a little bit afraid because I still remembered how I'd felt here when I was seven. But now that I'd gone up the elevator and down the stairs over and over again, I knew how to find my way out of there.

I walked down the hall quickly — I started running as I got close to the end — then I opened the door to the staircase and ran down to the ground floor.

My father was waiting for me by the elevator.

"Now I want you to do that two more times," he said, "and then I have a surprise for you."

I did it. I took the elevator up and ran down the stairs two more times. Then I went to the elevator (and believe me, I was about as tired of the whole business as you must be tired of reading about it).

My father said to me, "Wait here for three minutes," and then he stepped aside and talked to somebody on his cell phone in a whisper.

I waited.

I heard him say, "Okay?" into the cell phone. Then he said to me, "All right, take the elevator up to the top floor again."

I got into the elevator and pushed the button. I rode up to the top floor, and the doors opened. But the hall wasn't dark.

It was all lit up, and my whole family was there, holding balloons and throwing candy at me as if it were my bar mitzvah.

Then I heard a bell ring. The elevator had already gone back down, and now it was back up again. The doors opened, and there in the elevator was my father, holding the handlebars of the mountain bike I'd been dreaming of for years.

"This is for you, Gadi," he said, and gave me a

kiss. "And I hope it changes your trauma into a wonderful experience."

*　　*　　*

And you know what? It really worked. All my fear went away. I'm not afraid of elevators anymore (although I don't play in them now) and I feel much more sure of myself than I used to.

I don't know where my father got his technique from, but I wanted to tell everybody about it, because I'm sure lots of kids have fears — they might be afraid of elevators, like I was, or they might be afraid of closed places, or of dogs, or even of people.

The only way to get rid of fear is to face the thing you're afraid of, over and over again, and to talk about it until you get used to it.

That's what I did, and I got rid of my fear.

Now, when I think of an elevator, two pictures come into my mind. Happy, laughing people throwing candy, and of course, a mountain bike!

And believe me — that feels a lot better than being scared.

Suspect

My name is Yossi.

I live in Ashdod, and I'm in fifth grade.

There are thirty kids in my class, and I'm friends with all of them, more or less.

This year, something happened to me, and I'd like to tell you about it, even though it brings back a lot of bad memories.

It was a cold, rainy day — a day I'll never forget.

Recess was over, and we were all going back into the classroom. Suddenly, someone yelled, "My Tetris! Where is it?"

Tetris is a computerized game, as you probably know. The kid doing the yelling was Binyamin.

We're not allowed to bring Tetris games to school. And if a kid does bring one, he doesn't shout about it. But Binyamin did.

He was able to get away with shouting about it,

because his Tetris was lost. If your Tetris disappears, that's enough of a punishment already, and no teacher is going to punish you again for something you *used* to have. Some rebbes might say, "You see, you got your punishment," but most of them wouldn't say even that. They'd let you figure it out for yourself.

Our teacher told Binyamin to search through his backpack for the Tetris. Binyamin looked for it, but it wasn't there. He told the rebbe he'd left it on his desk.

"Do you remember when you were last playing with it?" the rebbe asked.

Binyamin didn't answer right away. "Um... a little while before recess," he mumbled.

"In other words, during the lesson?"

"Um... yes, rebbe. I mean, I wasn't exactly playing with it, I only took it out," said Binyamin — even though we all heard his Tetris making noises during *shiur.* I think the rebbe heard it, too. But Binyamin looked so sad and embarrassed that the rebbe didn't mention it.

Binyamin's Tetris is actually a pretty quiet one. But if the player (that is, Binyamin) isn't doing well, it plays a little "loser's tune," like a tower falling down (you'll have to imagine it for yourself). So if

Binyamin had been a good player, we wouldn't have heard it during the lesson. But Binyamin isn't a good player, and that's why we all heard it. We all knew that, and the rebbe knew it, but this wasn't the time to rate him as a player. The Tetris had disappeared; that was the issue.

"Did you take the game out of the classroom?" the teacher asked.

"No," said Binyamin. "It was raining, and I didn't want it to get wet, so I left it on my desk."

"Boys, has anyone in the class seen Binyamin's Tetris?"

Silence.

"No one has seen Binyamin's Tetris?" said the rebbe. Going twice.

Silence.

"Then you'd all better take a look in your bags," said the rebbe.

When a teacher starts talking about looking in bags, things start getting tense, because that means that he thinks somebody took the game (and the kids think so, too), but he's trying to give whoever took it a last chance to "find" it and get out of the situation gracefully, instead of getting caught. But from my years of experience at school, I've learned that this tactic doesn't work too well, because any kid who would take something that doesn't belong to him would also tell the teacher that he looked for it and it wasn't in his bag.

I opened my bag and started looking. But then I heard the rebbe say, "No, boys, not like that. I want every boy to search the bag of the boy next to him."

Now, that was a refreshing change. And clever, too. A kid might "not find" a game that he took, but it's not too likely that he would help his desk mate hide something that he took from another kid.

We made the search, each kid looking in his partner's bag. But the Tetris wasn't found.

What now? We all wondered.

"Boys," said the rebbe. "I want you to try to remember. We're talking about a game that belongs to one of your classmates. *Chas v'shalom* that such a thing should happen in our class, that anyone should take something that does not belong to him."

Binyamin spoke up, "Maybe it's in somebody's coat pocket."

We hadn't thought of that. A coat pocket would make a good hiding place for a Tetris.

Our teacher starting searching the coats. He worked quickly, while we all watched him, holding

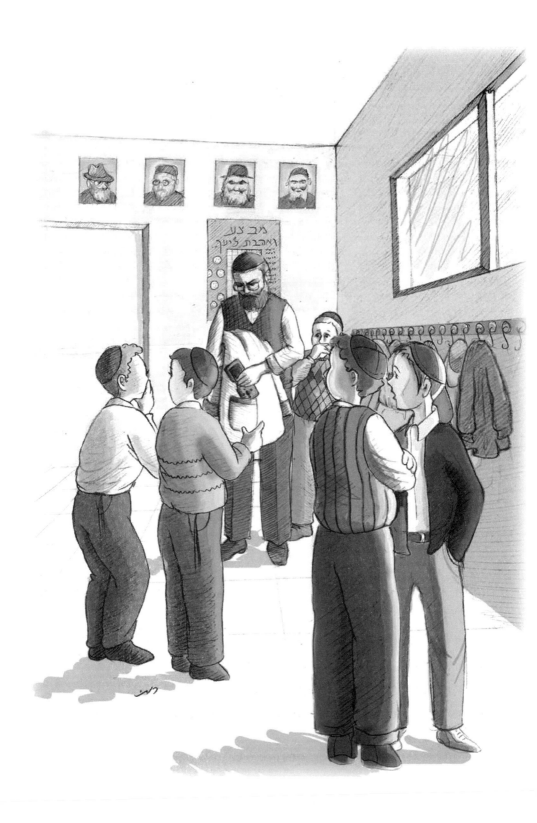

our breaths. He gave every coat a good squeeze all over, especially in the pocket area, and if he felt any hard object, he took that coat down from its hook and took out whatever it was...

In one coat he found a roll of paper. In another, he found a little hoop. In a third, he found a yo-yo. In a fourth, a pocket calculator. There were a lot of tense moments, and a lot of let-downs when he didn't find the Tetris.

Then he came to a tan coat. We watched, and saw his hands come up against something hard. He put his hand into the coat pocket and took out...

The Tetris. What else?

A murmur passed through the class. The rebbe looked at the name label in the coat, but none of the kids needed to look for the name. Who didn't recognize that tan coat with the black fur lining? Everybody knew whose coat it was.

Mine!

*   *   *

That's right. The Tetris was in my coat pocket.

That proved it, or so the kids thought: I was the one who took the Tetris.

Everyone looked at me. My face turned red, and my eyes filled with tears, I couldn't help it. I was so embarrassed. I wished I could bury myself. I put my head down on the desk and started to cry.

All around, I heard them whispering.

"Yossi! Who would've believed it?!"

"Why did he do it?"

"Boy, is he in trouble..."

Then the bell rang again for recess, and I knew what was about to happen. All the kids would go outside, and in a moment the whole school would "know" that Yossi was a thief. My two brothers would hear about it, too, and they would tell my parents. An alarm bell started ringing inside me. It was too much for me, I knew I couldn't take it. My whole body started shuddering, I started breathing hard, and a horrible fear crept over me.

The kids started getting up from their seats, but the teacher told them to stay. Everybody froze, and waited to hear what he was going to say.

"Yossi," he said, "could it be that you forgot the Tetris in your coat pocket?"

I knew he was trying to help me get out of it gracefully, but I didn't want to cooperate.

"No," I said, "I don't know who put the Tetris in my pocket."

Another murmur went through the room, and then everyone was babbling at once. I heard kids saying things like, "Right. The Tetris went for a little walk, and it jumped into your pocket." And, "Why don't you just admit the truth and let us all out of here?"

They were saying all sorts of things like that, things that really hurt my feelings, so I put my hand up and said, "Rebbe, I know that nobody's going to believe me, but I'm telling you, I didn't touch that Tetris. I didn't know where it was, and I was hoping it would be found just as much as everyone else."

No one said a word. The kids didn't know what to believe. I sounded very honest and convincing, but on the other hand... the Tetris was found in my pocket, and we all knew it didn't get there by itself.

Then the teacher said, "I have a story to tell you. I'll leave the choice up to you: Either you'll have recess or you'll hear the story."

Of course, everyone voted for the story. We all knew that this wasn't going to be just a story, but a true story, from real life, and that's something we don't get every day.

*　　　*　　　*

"Thirty years ago," the rebbe began, "something just like this happened in a fifth-grade class in another city. One of the boys had some candy, which was rare in those days, and it disappeared. A search was conducted, and the candy was found in the pocket of one of the boys' coats.

"That boy was punished severely for taking something that wasn't his. He had to take a note home to his parents, telling them what he'd done, and he was ordered to stay in the classroom during recess for a week.

"But that was the easy part of the punishment. The real punishment was that the boy was ostracized in class — that means everyone avoided him and no one would be his friend anymore.

"He got a reputation as a thief. As soon as he came into class, the boys would all hide their possessions from him, and if he got into an argument and the other boy couldn't think of anything else to say, he would call him a thief and win the argument that way.

"The boy grew up and went to a yeshivah where nobody knew him, and little by little, he tried to build himself up. It wasn't easy for him. He had suffered so much shame that he didn't have much self-confidence left. He'd been hurt so much that it was hard for him to study and to make friends.

"Years passed, and he started learning in *beis*

medrash, and eventually he got married and had a home of his own.

"One day, his telephone rang. It was someone who wanted to come and see him. He remembered the name — it was one of the boys who had been in his class years ago, when they were children. He hadn't heard from this boy since they'd both finished eighth grade. He didn't know where he had gone to study after that, or whom he had married.

"That evening, they met. They asked each other how they were, where they'd studied, and what they'd been doing throughout the years. After a while they ran out of things to talk about.

"An uncomfortable silence fell. It lasted for about a minute, and then the man said to his guest, 'I'm sure you must have come here with some purpose in mind...'

"The guest cleared his throat and said, 'Yes... I've been wanting to come and see you for awhile, but I didn't have the courage to do it. In fact, not a day has gone by that I haven't thought about pay-ing you this visit. Finally, I got up my courage, and here I am...'

"His host waited expectantly to hear what the visit was about, and then the visitor said, 'I don't know if you remember, but when we were kids, there was something that happened one day in school. Some candy was found in your coat pocket — candy that belonged to another kid. You were blamed for taking it. Maybe you've forgotten the whole incident. Do you remember anything about it?'

"'Yes, I remember,' said his host quietly.

"'Well, what I wanted to tell you is that I was the one who put the candy in your coat pocket. I picked it up from the desk; I think I wanted to check whether it had a *hechsher*, or something like that. And then all of a sudden the kid it belonged to came in and started yelling, "Somebody took my candy!" I got scared, so I put it in the nearest place I could find, which happened to be your coat pocket. I wasn't trying to pin the blame on you — it's just that your coat was the nearest one. I came here tonight to ask you to forgive me, even if you don't remember all the details.'

"The visitor was sweating a lot," the teacher continued. "It was hard for him to say all that. His host, of course, remembered the incident far better than the visitor had ever imagined.

"It wasn't easy for either of the two men to talk about it. They both felt very embarrassed. After a few moments, the host told the visitor that of course he was willing to forgive him, but it would take time, because the incident had left him with scars, and it wasn't easy to forgive wounds that went so deep.

"There was an awkward silence, and then the host said, 'You ask me if I remember the incident? I have to tell you that for all these years, there hasn't been a day — there's hardly been a minute — that I haven't thought about it. It isn't something I have to think back to try to remember. It's right here, inside me, all the time. It's part of me. But please tell me one thing: Why did you wait until now to come and talk to me about this?'

"'I can't explain it exactly,' said the visitor. 'But lately I've been making a *cheshbon nefesh*, I've been reviewing my deeds, and when I look at my life, it seems as if I got stuck at some point in my youth. I'm not married yet, and most of my friends already have seven or eight kids. I've been lonely and unhappy for years. So I decided I'd better make a *cheshbon nefesh* and try to figure out why I've been having so much trouble.

"'I looked far back into my past, trying to re-member if I'd hurt someone and not been forgiven for it. I really couldn't remember anything very serious that I'd done to anybody. Then, all of a sud-den, out of the blue, this incident came back to me, and I thought to myself, who knows? It might have caused you a lot of pain and sorrow. So I decided I'd have to come and ask you to forgive me.'

"His host thought for a few moments. He was trying to make up his mind whether to tell the visitor just how much that simple incident had hurt him. Should he tell him it had affected his whole life? Finally he decided not to tell him. His friend hadn't intended to harm him, and his life was full of pain as it was.

"He decided to forgive him."

*   *   *

The teacher looked around at his students. "Do you wonder how I know all this?" he asked.

No one said a word.

"I know it because I was that boy," said the teacher. "Thirty years ago, someone slipped another boy's candy into my coat pocket, and I was unjustly accused of taking it. It was only a few weeks ago that he came to my house to ask me for *mechilah*.

"I had a question about all this. What had made my friend suddenly remember this incident? He had been a lonely bachelor for a long time. He must have wondered many times if he'd hurt someone, and if that was why he hadn't found a wife. Why did he remember it and finally get up the courage to come to me when he did?

"Today," said the rebbe, "my question was answered. Today, a Tetris game was found in the pocket of one of my *talmidim*, and Hashem made sure that this story wouldn't just be in the back of my mind, where it's been lingering for thirty years, but in the front of my mind, where it needed to be. Because I'm here now to warn every member of this class not to suspect an innocent person! I tell you, I believe Yossi with all my heart. He didn't take the Tetris. Someone else took it, whether on purpose or unintentionally. And I'm calling on that boy to come to me privately and admit the truth, so that Yossi will be cleared of suspicion once and for all. I promise the boy, whoever he is, that I will keep his identity a secret."

Then the rebbe let us go out to recess. I breathed a sigh of relief, but I still felt kind of strange, because it was only the teacher's word that saved me from being "ostracized." I wished there could be some clear proof that it really wasn't me who took the Tetris.

The next day, before the rebbe started the first lesson, he told us that one of the boys in class had come to him and confessed that he had played a prank. He had taken the Tetris and put it in my pocket as a joke. He hadn't meant to cause trouble for me; he was just trying to play a trick on Binyamin.

As they say, all's well that ends well. I breathed a big sigh of relief.

But sometimes I still wonder how this story would have ended if all that stuff hadn't happened to the teacher when he was a kid, and he hadn't told that story. Everybody would still be suspecting me. It makes me feel awful just to think of it. It makes me feel so bad that I try to forget the whole thing.

But on second thought, I don't think I should forget it. Because if a situation like this comes up again in the future, I want to remember not to jump to conclusions. Especially conclusions like that — conclusions that could ruin another kid's life.

The Third Plague

My name is Naama.

I'm eleven years old, and I'm in fourth grade.

Before I start my story, I want to warn you: It's going to make your head itch. If you don't believe me, read on and you'll see.

One day, I came home from school and sat down to do my homework.

My mother was sitting next to me, helping me, and suddenly she said, "Naama, do you realize you're scratching your head all the time?"

I hadn't really noticed I was scratching so much, but now that she mentioned it, I remembered that it had been bothering me for days — an itchy, crawly feeling all over my head. I was already used to it. I thought I just had an itchy scalp, and that was all.

But my mother said knowingly, "I think you may have lice."

"Lice? Why should I have that?" I was shocked. I had lice once when I was a little kid in nursery school, but big kids don't get lice — or do they?

Ima didn't argue with me. She said, "Let's take a look, and then we'll know better."

She took the small, fine-toothed comb that she uses for my little sister (she's *always* getting lice) and she ran it through my hair a few times. Then she said, "Oh, boy, have you got them."

She showed me the comb, because she knew I wouldn't believe her unless I saw them with my own eyes. And there they were: two disgusting little creatures wriggling on the comb — and they had come from my hair. I had to admit it, I had lice.

In the next five minutes, Ima removed five more nasty lice from my hair, plus some eggs they had laid. If she hadn't taken the eggs out, they would have hatched and added new members to the family of lice that had moved in on my head.

That night I went to bed clean, shampooed, scrubbed, and combed. There wasn't a chance of any more lice in the vicinity.

Or so I thought.

But that's not the way it worked out.

Two days later, I sat down in the living room to do my homework once again, and suddenly I found myself scratching my head. This time, it wasn't my mother who mentioned it to me; I noticed by myself that I was scratching.

I went and asked Ima to take another look and see if I had any more lice.

She took the comb and checked, and she found two lice.

"Naama," she said, "lice don't grow in your hair by themselves. They have to come from somewhere. There must be a plague of lice going around in your class. You've been struck with *Makkas Kinim*, the third plague of Egypt. I want you to be careful not to get too close to anyone else's hair when you're in school. Lice move from one head to another."

I had to go through the whole lice-removing process all over again. It's not much fun, especially the combing. The comb digs into your scalp and pulls your hair, although my mother does it as gently as possible. First I shampoo my hair and put conditioner on it. The conditioner is slippery, and it makes some of the lice loosen their grip and come out easily. The rest have to be removed with the fine-toothed comb. The conditioner helps with that, too, since it softens the hair and untangles it, so Ima doesn't have to pull so hard on the comb.

Another good thing about all this is that it gives

me a chance to be alone with Ima and talk. So it's *almost* a nice, relaxed time to be together — only it's interrupted now and then by a loud "ouch" from me, when Ima digs in a little too deep or pulls a little too hard with the comb.

The problem was that we started having to do this practically every day. Every day or two we were finding another couple of lice. It wasn't just a case of lice that you take care of, and you're rid of it. It was the third plague of Egypt, like Ima said.

"Look around the classroom and see who's scratching," Ima suggested. "And avoid getting too close to those girls."

As soon as she said, "see who's scratching," I knew who was giving me lice all the time.

Etty. She shares a desk with me, and she's my best friend.

*   *   *

I didn't say anything to my mother about Etty. I decided that before I made up my mind about who was giving me lice, I should pay careful attention to what went on in school.

And the next day, that's just what I did. I watched carefully. Boy, did I watch carefully. Etty was scratching so hard that I was afraid she'd hurt herself. I peered into her hair when she wasn't looking, and with my own eyes I saw a whole zoo of lice, and plenty of eggs, too.

It was no wonder I kept getting lice. How could I not get them? We sit next to each other, we talk to each other, and sometimes we tell secrets; and of course you can't tell a secret in class without leaning close to the other girl's ear. Now do you see why I kept getting them again and again?

Speaking of secrets, Etty leaned towards me at that moment as if she was reading my mind and whispered, "You'll never guess what happened last..."

I pulled away from her. I felt as if a swarm of lice were crawling from her head to mine.

Etty couldn't understand why I pulled away and stopped listening. She looked at me in surprise. "Don't you want to hear my story?" she said.

"Not now," I answered.

She looked a little hurt. She wasn't used to being put off like that. How could she know that I had a reason — not just one reason, but a lot of *little* reasons — not to let her get too close to me?

At recess, we started playing, but I couldn't relax and let myself go, because all the time I had to remember not to get too close.

By the end of the day, I was very tired. It had taken a lot of effort to remember to keep my distance, and it wasn't easy, because like I said, Etty is my best friend and we're always together. I didn't want to hurt her feelings, so I kept worrying about how to keep a distance without letting her notice it. I came home exhausted.

To make things even worse, after all my efforts, when my mother checked me for lice that evening, she found a few! I wasn't exactly thrilled about that.

*   *   *

A few days passed, and every day the same thing happened. Etty was full of lice and scratching all the time, and when I got home, Ima would check and find a new "guest" on my head.

My mother decided to call my teacher and ask her to talk to the class about the problem. If she would tell the girls to ask their mothers to start checking them for lice every day, we figured that the problem would be solved for the whole class.

The teacher spoke to the class. But I think Etty must have forgotten about what the teacher said.

By the way, I should've mentioned that Etty isn't the kind of kid who doesn't care about being clean.

I'm sure she showers every day. But to get rid of lice, being clean isn't enough. After shampooing, you have to use a fine-toothed comb to get them out, and that was what Etty wasn't doing.

Things started getting very tense between Etty and me. I was starting to feel really disgusted by her, even though she was my best friend. She lived near me and she'd played with me all my life, and we always got along well, but now things were changing. Suddenly, after all these years, I was keeping a distance from her, and it made me feel awful. I soon found out that it made her feel even worse.

At twelve o'clock recess, she came over to me. "Naami," she said, "can I talk to you for a second?"

"Of course," I said, trying to look surprised.

"What's the matter between us?" she asked.

"What do you mean?" I said, trying to stall for time.

"I mean, I've noticed that you've been, kind of, keeping away from me."

"Keeping away from you?" I asked, trying to sound shocked. That worked about as well as trying to look surprised when she asked to talk to me. In other words, she could tell I was faking it.

"Oh, come on, Naama. What's the story?"

"I have no idea what you're talking about, Etty."

"All right, then," she said. "When you decide you have an idea of what I'm talking about, then I'll talk to you." And she walked away.

There I was in the schoolyard, knowing I had a big problem now with Etty. Maybe I'd solved one problem — at least now she wasn't coming near me — but now I had another problem: She *wouldn't* come near me. Or at least, not until I explained to her what was going on.

I walked home alone. I've never walked home from school alone — unless either Etty or I was sick, or something like that, but never because she was mad at me.

When I got home, I did my homework and Ima checked through my hair, as usual. That day, she didn't find any lice.

"Not a louse in the house," she said. "You've got a problem-free head."

But I didn't have a problem-free head. What could be a worse problem than having your best friend mad at you, and having no idea what to do about it?

Of course, I could have just gone over to Etty and said, "Listen, Etty. The problem is that you've got lice." But I knew I could never do that. She would probably feel very insulted and hurt. I thought of writing her an anonymous letter — that would save me the awkwardness of telling her to her face. But it wouldn't be a nice thing to do; it would hurt her even more than just telling her directly. My father once told me that *makeh re'ehu b'seser*, striking one's fellow man secretly, is a very serious transgression, because it doesn't even give the person a chance to defend himself. So I wasn't going to go and leave her a note like that. But what *was* I going to do, then?

Meanwhile, Ima had noticed that something was wrong between me and Etty. She asked me why we weren't calling each other on the phone or going to each other's houses. I made some vague excuse and didn't tell Ima what was going on. I kept all the pain and worry inside.

* * *

A few more days went by, and my classmates started noticing it, too. After all, we were the closest pair of friends in the class, and now we weren't even speaking to each other. When two good friends have a fight, the girls start talking about black cats. "I heard that a black cat passed between you," Efrat taunted me. "A big, fat black cat!" Efrat is an expert on black cats and on all the latest gossip about friends breaking up.

I didn't answer her, but I said to myself, *It only takes a few little lice to ruin a great friendship.*

I went home very sad that day. I sat in my room brooding. All of a sudden, I realized that I just *had* to find a solution to this problem. This break-up with Etty was much worse than having my hair pulled with a fine-toothed comb every day.

So what am I going to do? I thought. *Do I have to have lice all the time for the rest of my life, just so I can be friends with Etty?*

I realized that if I had told her nicely, before all this happened, it would have been all right. But if I told her now, she would be so insulted! She would feel so rejected!

I didn't know what to do, and automatically I started saying a chapter of *Tehillim* that I always say when I'm in trouble: "*Shir hama'alos...me'ayin yavo ezri?* — where will my aid come from?"

As soon as I finished, the solution to the whole problem popped into my head.

I got up and ran straight to Etty's house. My heart was pounding as I knocked on the door. I wasn't sure how Etty was going to react when she saw me. She came and answered the door.

We looked at each other without saying a word. Finally, Etty said, "What do you want?"

"I... I want to talk to you, Etty. But not in the house. Could you come outside, please?"

Right away, she stepped out and closed the door. I could see she wanted to settle our problem as much as I did.

We went and sat on our favorite bench, and then I said to her, "Etty, you were right. I *have* been keeping away from you. But it's not because I wanted to hurt you. In fact, it's just the opposite."

"But you did hurt me," she said.

"But I didn't mean to," I said. "I had another reason."

"Another reason? You were trying to do me some kind of favor, I suppose?"

She sounded very hurt, but I went ahead and said, "Yes, that's what I was trying to do, Etty."

"What good was I supposed to get out of that? Having my best friend suddenly reject me, and everybody talking about us and saying we broke up, and being left lonely," she said with tears in her eyes. "How exactly was all that supposed to help me? It doesn't make any sense!"

"I know it doesn't make sense, Etty. That's why I came. I want to explain."

She quieted down and looked at me, waiting to hear what I had to say.

"Lately, I've... I've been having a certain problem, and until it goes away, I have to keep a bit of a distance from you."

"What's the problem?" Etty asked.

"It's kind of embarrassing," I said, and took a deep breath. "The problem is, I've got lice. And I was afraid you might catch them from me."

"Lice? How did you get lice? That's something little kids get from playing in the sandbox."

"I don't know, but my mother found them in my hair, and I didn't want you to catch them. I was embarrassed to talk about it, but to tell you the truth, I'm afraid I may have given them to you already."

"You know something?" said Etty. "Lately, I *have* noticed that my head has been itching a lot. Maybe I really did catch them from you!"

"Do you understand now, Etty?" I asked. "I didn't know what to do. I was ashamed to tell you I had lice, but I didn't want you, my best friend, to catch them from me. And that was why I was trying not to come too close to you."

She sighed with relief. "So that's all that was wrong. But what are we going to do about it?"

"Well, I think that first of all, you should check and find out if you already caught them from me. And meanwhile, until I get rid of my problem, we should be careful not to come too close to each other, because lice can pass from one person's head to another."

"You're such a good friend," said Etty. "Now I see what was going on. You really were keeping away from me for my own good. But how could I have known it was because of something like that? I never would have thought of such a thing. Anyway, you're right — I'd better go and ask my mother to take a look at my hair. And for now, we'll keep a bit of a distance between your head and mine! I hope you get rid of the lice fast!"

We parted on good terms. In fact, I think we were even closer than before, and I was happy that I'd solved the problem.

Now Etty would go to her mother, she'd find out that she had a bad case of lice, and it would be taken care of. She would stop itching, and in the meantime, she would keep her distance from me, thinking that it would prevent her from getting them again.

Baruch Hashem, everything was working out.

*　　　*　　　*

That night, before I went to sleep, Ima came and sat down next to my bed.

"Naama, you're a little *tzaddeikes*," she said. "You're absolutely incredible."

"What do you mean?" I said.

"Not only are you a *tzaddeikes*, but you're very smart, too. That was a wonderful thing you did today."

"What wonderful thing?" I asked, wondering how she could possibly know what happened with Etty.

"Etty's mother called, and she said you're a fantastic girl. In fact, she said more than that. She said you have a 'noble spirit.' She told me she checked Etty's hair today, and it was absolutely crawling with lice. She was *very* impressed with the way you told Etty about it, even though it was embarrassing for you, and the way you tried to keep her from catching it from you. She said I've done a great job of raising you," said Ima with a smile. "But she doesn't know the whole story. She doesn't know how big a *tzaddeikes* you really are. Only you and I know that you made it sound as if *you* were the one with the problem, so that you wouldn't hurt Etty's feelings. I'm want you to know how proud of you I am. I'm especially impressed by your good *middos* and how clever you are."

136

I didn't say anything. What could I say?

Then Ima told me a few stories about people who were willing to suffer all sorts of pain and embarrassment in order not to put another person to shame. Then she gave me a big hug and complimented me a few more times, until I really didn't know what to do.

I fell asleep with a big smile on my face. The lice were gone, and instead, I had a lot of good feelings in my heart.

* * *

I apologize to you readers if my story made you itch. If it did, there are two possible reasons for it. The first is psychological. Talking or reading about lice makes people start itching, even if they don't have lice. Just the thought of lice makes them itch. I even felt itchy while I was writing this story.

But there could be another reason. I don't like to say this, but if you're itching really badly, it just might be that... you might happen to have lice. Maybe you'd better check — just to make sure. After all, it happens in the best of families.

Cherem

My name is Bentzy.

I live in Jerusalem, and I'm in seventh grade.

My story happened last year, when I was in sixth grade. It's hard for me to write this, because it brings back such bad memories. But even though it hurts, I want to write it anyway — both for myself and for all the kids who will read it.

I'm what you might call a very lively kid. I've always got ideas for things to do, and I love to laugh and play. Ever since nursery school I've been thought of as a likable kid. I've never fought with my friends, except little fights that are over in ten minutes, and I never had to fight for my position in class — because I had a good position without fighting for it.

The years go by so fast that I can hardly remember them. But last year was a year I'll never forget.

Cherem

At the beginning of my sixth-grade year, a new kid named Nachum joined our class, and naturally everyone wanted to meet him. And after that, they all wanted to be his friend, because he was a very sociable, interesting kid. He had so many stories to tell, everyone would stand around fascinated, just listening to him. Very soon, he'd made a place for himself in our class group.

Not only did he make a place for himself, he even became the center of a group of kids who hung around with him at recess and after school. I guess the rest of us noticed it, but it didn't seem very important.

One day when I was on my way home, I saw Nachum, surrounded by a crowd of kids, passing by old Shimon's vegetable store. One of them pushed over a crate as he passed by, and all the vegetables scattered all over the sidewalk.

Some people on the street looked at them angrily, but they just laughed and ran away to the other side of the street, where I was walking.

I saw old Shimon looking at his vegetables, scattered everywhere. He clapped his hands together in aggravation.

I felt sorry for him, and I decided to go and help him pick up the vegetables.

I crossed the street and started picking them up, when suddenly, from behind me, someone pinched me.

"Hey, that hurts!" I yelled.

"It's supposed to hurt, you hooligan!" said a voice. I turned around and saw that it was Shimon. Then he lifted me up with both hands and held me in the air.

"What do you want from me?" I asked.

"What do I want, you ask? You've got a nerve asking me that, you hooligan."

"Let me go!" I said.

"I'll let you go when you and your friends stop knocking over my merchandise," he yelled.

"But it wasn't me! I'm not one of them."

"Oh, so you just happened to be walking by, and you don't even know them, huh?" he told me sarcastically.

"I know them, but I'm not with them. They're in my class, but I wasn't involved. I just wanted to help you, that's all."

A lady who was standing nearby came over to Shimon and said, "That's right. He's telling the truth. He was on the other side of the street, and when they ran away, he came running over here to pick up what they spilled."

Shimon looked surprised for a second, then he put me down and said. "I apologize, I didn't realize. It's just that those kids are driving me crazy. They're ruining my health. Every day, they come around making trouble."

"I'm sorry," I said. "Maybe I can try to talk to them."

I started picking up vegetables, and then I heard a voice yelling, "Bentzy the greengrocer! Bentzy the greengrocer!"

It was the kids from my class, making fun of me from the other side of the street.

*   *   *

But that was only the beginning.

The next day when I came to school, I was greeted by shouts of "Bentzy the greengrocer! Bentzy the greengrocer!" My classmates were saying that they saw me working in a vegetable store, and they were all laughing at me. Nobody bothered to mention that I was helping an old man clean up the mess they'd made. They just wanted to make me into a laughingstock.

Then, to make things even worse, the principal came in just then and asked some of the boys to come into his office.

All of them were in the gang that had knocked over the vegetables.

They came back a half an hour later. All of them except for one: Nachum, the new kid. They looked at me very angrily, and I realized they must be thinking that I told the principal on them.

In the middle of the lesson, I started hearing whispers.

"Tattletale!"

"Informer!"

But they saved the real thing for recess.

The moment *shiur* was over, they all started yelling at me. "You're an informer, that's what you are. Because of you, they suspended Nachum from school! We're gonna get you, just wait and see!"

A couple of them started hitting me, but most of them just used words, and they made sure to tell everyone they could what a tattletale I was, and how they should stay away from me.

Nachum came back to school after two days, and that was when my troubles really began.

*   *   *

The first thing he did was to gather most of the class around him and tell them that they were putting me in *cherem* — from now on, no one was allowed to talk to me. Not a word. He told them not to let me join any of their games and not to sit next to me.

I was a bit too far away from them to hear what they were saying, but I could see they were talking about me. And I don't know how to describe how that made me feel.

From that moment on, I was ostracized. Everyone snubbed me completely. I tried going over to some of the kids, but they ignored me. To make matters worse, they told other kids that I'd tried to talk to them and that they wouldn't let me, and they all laughed about it. I went over to a few of the nice, quiet kids in the class. I thought they would talk to me, but they told me they were afraid to, because the whole class had decided to snub me.

"But it's not the whole class," I said. "It's just one kid who's been here only a month."

They just shrugged their shoulders and walked away.

There I was, abandoned and lonely, after years of being one of the leaders of the class. All of a sudden no one would talk to me. They wouldn't even come near me.

After a few days I tried again to break down the barrier they'd put up against me, but Nachum was very bossy, and warned them not to show me any mercy. He threatened the kids that if anyone was caught saying a word to me, that kid would be banned, too. But at the same time, even though they weren't talking to me directly, they still managed to insult me constantly.

I was coming home every day with a sad face, and every morning I was scared to go to school because I didn't know what they might do to me.

My parents noticed that I was constantly in a gloomy mood, but they didn't know why. I made a big mistake by not telling them right away.

But in the end they found out anyway. One of the neighbors told my mother that she saw me walking to school with a whole gang of kids behind me calling me a greengrocer. That day when I came home, my mother asked me what that was all about, and all of a sudden I burst out crying, and I couldn't stop.

She was startled to see me so upset, and she asked me to tell her about it, but I couldn't do anything but cry. I could hardly breathe, I was sobbing so hard.

Still not knowing what the problem was, my mother called my teacher. But he didn't know what was going on, either. The next day, he spoke with a few of the kids, and very quickly he found out the whole story.

During recess, he spoke with Nachum and told him to stop this whole business of ostracizing me. Nachum gave him a sneaky answer: He said he hadn't forced the other kids not to talk to me, but if he personally didn't want to talk to me, he didn't have to.

The teacher wasn't satisfied with that. He made Nachum tell the class that the *cherem* was canceled. But it didn't do any good. Nachum repeated the rebbe's words, but with his eyes he made it clear to the kids what he *really* wanted them to do. There were a few naive kids who thought he really meant what he said, but when they tried to talk to me, the class stopped talking to them, and that set them straight pretty fast.

Things got even worse. I felt all torn up inside. And I was getting so depressed that I didn't know what to do with myself. I wondered how I could continue to get up in the morning and how long I could go on facing being ridiculed all the time.

It seemed like Nachum was thinking up something new every day. He was ruining my life. I started really hating him; I wished all sorts of awful things would happen to him. I know that might shock you, but I want you to know that that's how someone feels when he's being hurt and tormented day after day.

I would pray to Hashem all the time to help me, but my prayers didn't seem to be getting answered. I felt broken, hurt, and alone.

My parents didn't know what to do. I knew they had spoken with the principal at my *talmud Torah*, and with my teacher. I knew that the teacher had talked with my class one day when I wasn't there. But none of this was helping. In fact, things were getting even worse.

* * *

One day, I was called to the principal's office.

My parents were there with the principal, and so was the vice-principal and my teacher. They asked me to tell them the whole story of how this situation had developed.

At first I was too embarrassed to say anything, but after a few minutes I got up the courage to speak. I started telling them all about how I used to be considered one of the leaders of the class until Nachum joined the class. Then I told them what had happened that day at the greengrocer's store, and about all the terrible things the class had been doing and saying to me ever since then.

When I talked about how mean they'd been to me, my mother started to cry and even my father looked teary-eyed. When I came to the part about the class following me and yelling "greengrocer," I could see that the principal and vice-principal were really upset.

The principal stood up at that point and said in a very emotional voice, "In my school, abuse like this will not be tolerated. I promise you I will put an end to this. And I want that to be clear: I didn't say I will *try* to end this, I said I *will* put an end to this, and I'll do it even if I have to suspend your entire class and put you in the other class — although I'm sure I won't need to go to that extreme."

Then he gave me a hug, clapped me on the shoulder, and promised me once more that this was the end of my suffering.

The next day, Nachum didn't come to school.

The principal came to our classroom and told us that Nachum had been expelled from the *talmud Torah*, and that any boy who hurt another boy would be suspended on the spot, with no discussion.

He didn't mention my name, but everyone knew who he was talking about. He talked about *sinas chinam*, baseless hatred, and how that was the reason our *Beis HaMikdash* was destroyed. He told us the story of Kamtza and Bar Kamtza — how Kamtza was supposed to be invited to a banquet and a servant went and invited Bar Kamtza by mistake. He described in a very lifelike way how Bar Kamtza must have felt when he was thrown out of the banquet. All the kids could see how upset the principal was, and they were really scared. They realized what terrible things they'd been doing and that Hashem punishes people for acting that way.

The principal warned the class very sternly to make sure no one would have any reason to complain of being treated badly. He emphasized, "Not only are you to be careful not to hurt anyone; you're to see to it that no one should even have cause to think you're treating him badly."

I understood what he meant by that. The kids had been abusing me in ways that I couldn't always prove. For example, what can you say about a kid who stands there making weird eye movements at you? He can always say, "My eyes were hurting, so I was blinking." And that was why the principal said what he did. He wanted his warning to be very clear.

A week later, Nachum came back. His parents had put pressure on the school to give him another chance. They had met with the principal and were told what their son had done. They were very upset to hear it, but they still claimed he shouldn't have been punished so severely without a warning. So Nachum was allowed to come back to school on probation. After a couple of days, however, he was already trying to organize something against me again, and he was immediately suspended for a week.

The next time he tried it, they told him that he was permanently expelled from the *talmud Torah*, and he never came back.

It's been a year since then.

It took the kids months to really understand what had happened. Nachum had a powerful personality, which he used in the wrong way, and the other kids were scared of him. That was why they tried to stay on his good side, even if it meant doing things they knew they shouldn't.

Anyway, the tough position the principal took saved my life. It really did. I don't know what kind of shape I would have been in by the end of the year if that mental abuse had continued.

One thing I know is that in many schools there are mean kids like that. That's why I decided to write about what happened to me, because I hope other kids will read it and see that they shouldn't let themselves be controlled by such a kid, even if he has a strong personality and they're afraid of him.

While I sit here writing, I know that hundreds of boys out there (and girls, too) are suffering abuse from other kids. I want them to read my story so they'll know they shouldn't keep everything bottled up inside. They *have* to tell their parents, and their parents should talk to the principal of their school. Situations like this can't be allowed to go on.

After I opened up and told the adults what was happening to me, the principal was able to take care of it. I got back to my old position in the class, all the kids are my friends, and everything is like it was before.

Well, not really everything.

I'm not the same kid that I was before all this happened.

I think I've become more sensitive to other people's feelings, because I found out from experience what it's like to be on the receiving end of abuse.

I've made a promise to myself: For the rest of my life, I'm going to help kids who are being hurt by their classmates.

This story is the first step in my career.

The Greatest Compliment

My name is Avichai.

I live in Ashdod, and I'm in seventh grade.

On *Rosh Chodesh Cheshvan*, my rebbe came into the classroom and announced that we were going to learn *Maseches Kiddushin* and that there would be a contest for the most beautiful notebook. Our notebooks would be judged for good handwriting, clear content, a beautiful title page, and a nice cover. The prize, he said, would be a deluxe set of *Mishnayos*.

As soon as this announcement was made, everybody turned around and looked at Yaakov.

Yaakov is the artist of our class. He's got hands of gold, as they say, and ever since first grade, he's always made the nicest decorations for our classroom. His notebooks have always been something special. We all heard the rebbe say it was a contest, but nobody really thought of it as a contest.

Of course Yaakov would have the most beautiful notebook. Every year we had a contest like this, and Yaakov always won. As far as we were concerned, the *Mishnayos* were already his. Why should we even bother trying to compete with him?

Motti raised his hand. "Rebbe," he said, "is there any chance of a second prize and maybe even a third prize?"

We all laughed.

"What is so funny about Motti's question?" the rebbe wanted to know.

That made us laugh even more.

"Would someone please explain?" The rebbe sounded really curious.

We all took a few seconds to calm down, and then Yoni volunteered to explain. Yoni is our class spokesman. No one ever appointed him to the job, it's just understood that he's the spokesman, just as Yaakov is the artist.

"Motti asked if there would be other prizes, because the first prize is sure to go to Yaakov," Yoni explained.

"Why do you think so?" asked the rebbe.

"Because Yaakov has won this contest every year since first grade!" said Yoni. "Not that we're jealous of him, rebbe. He really deserves the first prize every time, because he's the best."

The rebbe held on to his beard and thought for a moment. "If that's how it is, and if Yaakov earns the first prize again this time, then I think we'll have to offer *two* first prizes. Otherwise, you'll feel there's no contest. And we'll offer second and third prizes, too. How does that suit you?"

That suited us just fine. Since first grade we've never had a real notebook contest, and now we were finally going to have one, with a fair chance for everybody.

That afternoon I went and bought a new notebook. It wasn't just a regular notebook; it was a special, leather-bound one. I spent hours working on a design for the front page. I wrote *Maseches Kiddushin* in fancy Hebrew letters and colored them with lots of different colors. It was a real work of art.

But that was only the beginning. Now I had to fill up the notebook with good, clear notes, and they had to be written in good, clear handwriting, without any crossing out or erasing to spoil the look of the page.

The pages had to be smooth, too, without any wrinkles or dog-ears.

The next day we started using our new notebooks. But I didn't write straight into mine. Every day I would write a draft of the questions in a regular notebook, and then at home I would write them over very neatly in my leather-bound notebook. I would write the date at the top of the page, and highlight my headings. I would do that by writing the words, "Questions" and "Answers" in different colors, and then I would underline them, using a ruler to make sure the lines were straight. It wasn't easy. I'm no artist, and it took me a long time to do all this. I had to be super-careful not to slip while drawing those lines, so they wouldn't come out crooked or touch any of the letters.

One night while I was working hard on my notebook, my sister came along and looked over my shoulder. "Only girls take so much trouble over their notebooks," she said. I'm not sure if she was trying to insult me, but to me it sounded like a compliment.

Ten pages were filled, then fifteen pages — summaries, review questions, tables and charts — I did everything very slowly and patiently, and put a lot of effort into it.

My classmates could see that I was trying for the first prize — the second first prize, that is — the first one after Yaakov. They starting encouraging me and cheering me on, and they gave me compliments on my style and my handwriting. But the biggest compliment of all was that they started asking if they could copy from me — mostly they wanted to copy my summaries, which we're allowed to copy from others. I really did try hard to make them clear and understandable, and a lot of kids used my material to prepare for tests and reviews.

Of course I told them to be very careful with my notebook, and not to let it get damaged. They understood what a treasure it was to me, and they treated it like a piece of expensive china.

*   *   *

The month of Cheshvan went by, and then came Kislev and Teves. Everyone was looking forward to Tu B'Shvat; that was the day the rebbe would be choosing the winners.

I was getting more and more excited and full of suspense. I treated that notebook like my most precious possession, because that's exactly what it was. I would wrap it up in padding, put it in a plastic bag, and then I would gently put it in a separate pocket inside my backpack. I was extra-special careful not to leave my backpack unguarded in the street even for a moment, because any bag left lying around looks suspicious, and the police bomb squad might come and blow it up — along with my precious notebook.

I didn't feel so sure of winning. There were at least five other kids who had notebooks just as nice as mine. In my heart, I believed that I had put more work into mine, but the rebbe might not know that. The suspense was almost unbearable, and it got worse as the fateful day came closer.

My father started putting limits on the amount of time I was allowed to spend working on my note-book. He said everything had to have limits. But after he left the room one day, I heard my mother say to him, "Maybe we should just let him be. He wants that first prize so badly." My father muttered something and didn't argue with her, so from that I understood that my parents also hoped I would win.

Rosh Chodesh Shvat came. Only fifteen days to go! The suspense was at its height. My notebook had fifty pages filled, and I had put hours of work into every one of them.

*　　　*　　　*

Then came the day I'll never forget. At ten o'clock I went out to the schoolyard for recess like everyone else, and when the bell rang and I came back into the classroom, I saw a group of boys crowded around my desk.

"Here he comes... he's here..." I heard voices saying, and I could tell that something very bad had happened. I went over to my desk. Five kids moved aside to let me through, and they all looked like they were in shock. I stepped up to the desk, and I saw a sight that hit me like a thunderbolt.

My beautiful, beloved notebook, that I had worked so hard on, was lying open on my desk, and somebody had scribbled all over it.

No one said a word. I picked up the notebook with shaky hands and starting leafing through it. I couldn't believe my eyes.

Whoever had done this had done a very thorough job. He didn't just scribble on one page. Ten pages were completely covered with scribbles — up and down and across the page and in circles and triangles. It looked like he was trying to wipe my work off the face of the earth.

I started to cry right there in front of everyone. I wasn't even ashamed. I knew no one would think I was a baby, because they all knew how much time

and effort I had put into that notebook. I wasn't crying just because my work was all lost now; I was also crying because I couldn't see what I'd done to deserve this, or why anyone would want to hurt me so much.

I just stood there and cried, and everyone stood around me, not knowing what to do or say. Then I saw the rebbe coming.

He came over, looked at the notebook, and then looked at me. He took it and leafed through it. I watched his face. It was turning stiffer and stiffer. His jaw was set, and his eyes were flaming.

When he finished looking at the notebook, he looked at me again, and all at once his expression became very soft and sympathetic.

He came closer and hugged me hard, but he didn't say anything.

Then he took the notebook to his desk, told the kids to sit in their places, and sat down with his head between his hands.

A tense silence filled the room. Everyone realized something terrible had been done. No one wanted to believe that there was someone in our class who could do a thing like that. It was really scary. Why would anyone want to do such a thing to a classmate?

The rebbe sat like that for a long time, holding his head between his hands. It must have gone on for about fifteen minutes, and it created a terrible atmosphere in the classroom. I was also sitting with my head between my hands. No one dared make a sound.

*   *   *

Suddenly, the rebbe got up. Everyone looked at him worriedly, wondering what he was going to do next. I kept my head between my hands, but I peeked out a bit between my fingers.

"Boys," he said, "I could have spoken to you now about the terrible thing we've all just seen, but I've decided not to do that. I don't like to speak to such young boys about jealousy and hatred and other corrupt *middos*. Instead, I am going to talk about good things.

"You all know that on Tu B'Shvat I was scheduled to announce the winner of our beautiful notebook contest. But that has changed. I can already announce the winner today, *Rosh Chodesh Shvat.*

"I've seen all of your notebooks almost every day. There were many fine contenders, and I could see that it wouldn't be easy to select the winner. But I'm sure I would have come to a decision in the end.

"Today, however, someone has made that choice for me, as the first-prize winner has already been selected. That anonymous boy has many *middos* to work on and correct, particularly the *middah* of *kinah*, jealousy. But let's focus for a moment on the victim he chose.

"Why would a boy go and scribble on another boy's notebook?" The rebbe raised his voice dramatically. "Because he wishes he could be like that boy. He wishes he could put in that much effort, work on it day and night, listen carefully in class, formulate clear answers and summaries, write drafts and patiently copy them, draw neat lines, and color everything in brightly. But he didn't, because he was too weak. He didn't find the strength in himself to put in all that effort, so instead, he chose to destroy someone else's work — the work that made him feel so weak and inadequate.

"And which work did he choose? Of course he looked for the one that reminded him, more than all the others, of the effort he could have made, but didn't. He chose the boy who worked the hardest on his notebook — the boy he wished he could be.

"Avichai," said the rebbe, "you shouldn't look at this scribbling as something that lessens the value of your work. On the contrary, this scribbling is the greatest compliment you could receive. It says a lot about you, not only about your work, but about your character. It says that someone — although we don't know who the scribbler is — wishes he could be just like you. There is someone in this room who admires you and your work very much — so much that he couldn't stand to see it, because it made him feel he was worth so much less than you. It's as if he were screaming, 'Avichai is the best! Avichai's notebook deserves first prize!'

"I hope that anonymous boy will draw the right conclusions and do *teshuvah* for his terrible deed. In any case, he has made it much easier for me to choose the first-prize winner. I announce right now that Avichai is our first-prize winner! Does anyone have any objections to that?"

"No-o-o!" shouted the class.

The rebbe called me up to his desk. I went up to the front of the room.

"Listen," he said to me, "I don't have the prize here today, because I didn't know I would be choosing the winner so soon. But for now, I want to give you the real prize — a prize that will accompany you all your life."

The rebbe handed me my notebook.

"Take good care of this notebook," he said. "Be

sure never to lose it — it's the highest honor you've ever received. Not the notebook itself as much as the scribbling. If you ever find yourself feeling weak or unable to tackle some task in life, go and look at these scribbles and remember that someone was once so jealous that he did this; and he was jealous because you were the best."

I'm so lucky to have a rebbe like him. He took the most awful thing that ever happened to me and turned it into the biggest compliment I'd ever received. I took my notebook home that day and told my parents what had happened. They were shocked and upset, of course.

But then I also told them everything the rebbe had said. That really worked. They calmed down, and my father said, "Your rebbe is a wise man. Not only did he make you — and us — feel better, but he also gave the right message to the class, and especially to the boy who committed this terrible act of jealousy. The things he said were much more effective than a speech about bad *middos*."

*   *   *

You probably think my story ends here.

But it doesn't. About one week later, someone put the following letter into my backpack:

> This is from me, I'm the one who scribbled on your notebook. I'm really sorry for what I did. I did it because I was jealous, and I want to ask you to forgive me. I also want to say that the rebbe was right. I only did it because you made the nicest notebook and you put the most work into it. Do you think you'll ever forgive me?

That whole day, I couldn't get that letter out of my head. After school, I showed it to the rebbe. He said he was very happy that the boy was sorry for what he'd done. I asked him if I should forgive the boy, and he said that if I felt that I was ready to forgive him, then I should do it with my whole heart.

The next week I found another note. It said:

> Do you forgive me? Please leave your answer in your notebook.

I wrote him an answer. I said that I wanted to forgive him, but I could only do it if I knew he had started to try and put his own effort into things instead of knocking down other people.

The next day he left me a long letter telling me how terrible he felt about what he'd done. One line he wrote really surprised me. He said that he was even worse than the rebbe said, and that he didn't like being that way and wanted to do *teshuvah*.

I couldn't understand how he could be even worse than the rebbe said. The rebbe had talked about a kid who was too weak to do something for himself, and so jealous that he destroyed someone else's work instead of making his own efforts. What could be worse than that?

After a few weeks of writing back and forth like this, he wrote that he would like to talk to me face to face. He said he knew this meant I would find out who he was, but he trusted me not to tell anyone.

I wrote that he should come to my house at eight o'clock that night, and I promised him that I wouldn't tell anyone who he was.

I went home and waited impatiently. I admit I was very, very curious to know who it was that had scribbled on my notebook. I knew a few things about him already: He had done a very ugly thing, but on the other hand, he really felt bad about it and he wanted to correct it.

At eight o'clock, the doorbell rang.

I ran to open it, and there stood...

Yaakov!

I was in shock.

Yaakov? This was the kid who always won first prize, ever since first grade! Out of the whole class, Yaakov was the one who'd ruined my notebook? It couldn't be! Why would *he* do a thing like that?

I brought him into my room, but I couldn't get a word out of my mouth. He looked very embarrassed, and he didn't say anything either.

Finally, I found my tongue, and I said, "Yaakov! You, of all people! But why?"

"Do you remember I wrote that what I did was even worse than the rebbe said?"

I nodded.

"Well, now you understand why."

I nodded again.

And then Yaakov started telling his story.

*   *   *

"As far back as I can remember," said Yaakov, "I was always number one. Hashem gave me talents and I used them, and I was always getting compliments and prizes. I never had to put a lot of effort into it; it came easily to me. And I got used to being number one. No one ever challenged my position.

"As soon as the rebbe said there were going to

be two first prizes, I felt a stab in my heart already. It was hard for me to make room for someone else up there at the top with me. It didn't seem fair. I didn't realize that this feeling came from a bad *middah*; I just felt it.

"The contest got underway, and the more you worked on your notebook, the more I could see that you were going to win the other first prize. I had no doubts about it; I knew it even before the rebbe did. I saw how hard you were working and how nice it was coming out, and I saw you really had talent. I even started to worry that you would win the first prize instead of me, and I would only get the 'second first-prize.'

"One day when I was feeling very upset about all this, I did that terrible thing. I ruined your work, and ever since that moment, I've been beating myself up inside. I keep thinking, *How could I have been so mean? How could I have let myself do such a thing?*

"The things the rebbe said that day really hurt me, because I knew how true they were. But the truth was even worse than the rebbe thought. He thought the kid who did it was someone who couldn't create a nice notebook of his own, so he went crazy with jealousy. I knew it was a kid who *could* create a nice notebook of his own, but he went crazy with jealousy anyway."

I didn't say anything. I never had anyone confess things like this to me before, and I didn't know what I was supposed to do. I knew there was no point in telling him what a bad thing he'd done. He knew that already. I wondered if I should try to say something encouraging.

While I was wondering, Yaakov said, "Could you tell me what I can do to make a *kaparah* for what I did? I want to make amends."

"I have no idea," I said. "I'm not a *rav*. I'm just a kid."

"Think about it," Yaakov insisted.

"Well..." I said, "I think it has to be something that's the opposite of jealousy, and the opposite of doing damage."

"Okay, I'll think about that," said Yaakov. "In the meantime, I take back my asking you to forgive me. After I make amends, maybe then I'll ask you."

*   *   *

Two days after that, the rebbe collected the rest of the kids' notebooks, so he could select the other prize-winners.

He went around the room, and when he came to

Yaakov's desk. It was empty. "Where's your note-book, Yaakov?" the rebbe asked.

"It's not here; I didn't bring it," said Yaakov. "I guess I left it home."

"Did you lose it?"

"No, I'm sure it's at home." Yaakov was being careful not to lie.

"You'll have to bring it by tomorrow, otherwise I won't be able to include you in the contest," said the rebbe.

"I understand that," said Yaakov.

Everybody in the class, except for me, thought this was just a technical problem. Yaakov had left his notebook at home, he would bring it tomorrow, and of course he would win the other first prize. I was the only one who realized that Yaakov wasn't planning to bring his notebook tomorrow. I could see what he'd decided to do in order to make amends.

Tu B'Shvat came, and the rebbe announced the winners. The other first-prize winner was... Eliyahu. He had worked very hard on his notebook.

Meir and Itzik won second and third prize.

Everyone was looking at Yaakov. He sat in his place, making a face that said, "What can I do? I forgot my notebook, and I'm paying the price for it." The kids all figured that Yaakov was so used to winning prizes that it wasn't a big deal for him anymore. Only I knew the truth.

Well, not only me. Someone else knew, too.

As soon as I could catch Yaakov alone, I went over to him. "I really admire you," I said. "That was a *kaparah* for what you did, for sure. Anyway... I think now I can say that I forgive you for everything that happened."

I clapped him on the shoulder, and he went out of the classroom. I stayed behind because I wanted to talk to the rebbe.

"I see that you've decided to forgive him," said the rebbe. "And it was very fine of him to give up his prize as a *kaparah* for what he did."

I was so surprised; I just stood there blinking for a moment. I hadn't told him that it was Yaakov.

"How did the rebbe know?" I blurted out.

"Oh, come on, Avichai," said the rebbe, "You showed me a handwritten note from Yaakov."

"But he didn't sign it!"

"Avichai, I've been teaching for thirty years, and even if you brought me a sample of handwriting from a student I had ten years ago, I would recognize it."

"But then... why didn't the rebbe do anything to Yaakov?" I dared to ask.

"When you grow up, Avichai, maybe you'll go into teaching, too, and then you'll understand that regret that comes from within the heart is much more meaningful than regret that you *make* a student feel. Just like you, I wished I knew who it was who had done such a terrible thing and displayed such bad *middos*. It was really bothering me. Then, when I saw the handwriting and realized who it was, I had conflicting feelings. On the one hand I was surprised, and I was very disappointed in him — a good student like that doing such a thing. But on the other hand, I was happy to see that he was expressing regret on his own, without being pushed into it. I preferred to leave it that way, and to observe Yaakov's *teshuvah* process from a distance."

The rebbe clapped me on the shoulder. "Anyway, Avichai, I'm still telling you to hang on to that notebook — especially the scribbling!" He gave me a big smile and winked at me.

* * *

I still have the notebook, and the scribbling too. And I have the *Mishnayos.* But besides that, I have an added bonus — I found out what a smart rebbe I have, and how much about life I can learn from him.

That's Another Story

My name is Michoel.

I'm eleven years old, and I live in Modiin Illit.

My story happened a few years ago, but I still remember it as if it happened yesterday.

First of all I should tell you that we're a Chassidic family. We are followers of a certain well-known rebbe, and my father and I usually go away for *Yom Tov* to be with him.

It was on Rosh Hashanah. My father and I traveled to Jerusalem, and we were staying in a big dormitory that the Chassidim had rented for all the people from out of town.

At the time, I was eight and a half.

Before *Minchah*, I was outside the *shul*, talking with some friends. Some of them I knew from the *talmud Torah* where I learn, and others I knew from my trips to Jerusalem with my father to be with the rebbe for *simchah*s and *Yamim Tovim*.

We were standing in a circle, talking, when all of a sudden, my friends starting running away from me. I didn't know why they were doing that.

At first I was going to run after them, but then I said to myself, *If they want to run away from me, let them. I'll act like I don't care.*

They ran until they were pretty far away and then they stopped and looked at me. I just stood there. I didn't move an inch.

One of my friends signaled to me to come over to him. I signaled right back to him that if he wanted me, he could come to me.

But he kept signaling to me to come, and all the rest of the kids started signaling, too. "Come on already, run!" one yelled.

I started thinking maybe I should run over to them, but I didn't want to. I thought they were just making fun of me, and that as soon as I ran to them, they would run away again.

So I stayed where I was.

"Look behind you!" my friend Tzviki yelled.

I turned and looked, and then I knew why everyone ran away.

The scariest-looking man I've ever seen was right behind me. He was dressed in rags, and he reminded me of the Cave Man from *Kids Speak 3*.

But there was a difference between them. This man looked like he was really not normal.

In a voice like thunder, he said to me, "So you want to run away from me, too?" and he stretched his hand out towards me. I was so scared, I started running like crazy, and I managed to reach my friends. They were relieved that I'd made it.

"Why did you stand there like that?" Tzviki asked me. "He almost caught you!"

They told me that all the kids in the neighborhood were terrified of this man, and every time they saw him coming, they would run away.

It took a few minutes for my heart to stop pounding. I was breathing hard, but I was happy that I'd managed to escape from him.

He started running towards us again. This time my friends didn't have to urge me. I ran like I'd never run before, until we reached the *shul* again.

One of the kids said, "Let's go look for him, and then run away from him again!"

Everybody thought that was a great idea, except for me. I said it sounded like kind of a mean thing to do. It reminded me of what the kids did to the Cave Man in that story.

"Oh, come on, you're just scared," said Shimi. He was right. I really was scared of that man. But even

without being scared, I still didn't think it was right — especially not right before Rosh Hashanah.

The kids listened to me, and the gang split up and started going home — either to their houses or to the dormitory if they were from out of town like me. I made sure I had someone to walk with, because I was scared that the man would jump out on me from some dark corner on the way.

*   *   *

That night, guess what I dreamed of? That man with the scary face, of course. In my dreams, he kept coming at me and yelling, "So you want to run away from me, too?" I kept waking up from this dream, and it took me a long time to go back to sleep again, even though I was very tired.

I was going to wake up my father, but I saw that he was sleeping deeply, and I knew we had to get up early in the morning, so I thought I'd better let him sleep.

I didn't know how I was going to get up so early, because I was only able to fall asleep at about four or five o'clock in the morning.

At six-thirty, my father tried to wake me up. I mumbled that I hadn't fallen asleep until after four o'clock, and my father said, "Sleep for another hour or two, then, and then get up and come to *shul* for 'HaMelech.'"

I went back to sleep.

I slept for at least two hours, and what woke me up was the silence. There wasn't a sound in the dormitory. I washed *neigel vasser* and got dressed. As I went downstairs to leave the building, I saw that there was nobody around. I was the only person in that whole big dormitory.

That was a scary feeling, being all alone there, so I started walking fast. I wanted to get out of there quickly.

When I got to the main door, I found out that I was in trouble. It was locked.

I knocked on the door and tried to pull it open, but it wouldn't budge; so I knocked some more.

Slowly but surely, it dawned on me that I was locked in. I was stuck all alone in this big, empty building, and I couldn't get out.

I started banging hard on the door, but pretty quickly I realized it was no use. The *shul* wasn't nearby, and there was nobody around. No one would hear me, no matter how much I banged and kicked.

I didn't know what time it was, and I didn't know why they'd locked me in.

I did a little more knocking and banging, and then I stood by the door and waited.

But if you think I've finished describing the nightmare, you're wrong.

That was only the beginning.

Suddenly I heard a rustling sound, then footsteps and voices murmuring.

So I wasn't alone after all. That was a relief. At least there was somebody around who could help me get out of here and go find my father in *shul*.

But I didn't feel relieved for long.

The corridor was dark and I couldn't see too well, so I just moved towards the sound of the footsteps. Then I saw someone come out of one of the ground-floor rooms. I took another step forward... and then I saw his face.

I heard a scream — it was me screaming.

The face was the face of the man who'd almost caught me the night before. It was an awful, scary face...

And he was coming towards me.

I couldn't move. I stood there, frozen to the spot. He came towards me... he almost reached me... then I suddenly remembered how to move and started running towards the stairs.

*   *   *

I ran up to the next floor, and then to the next. Then one more flight. That was where my room was, the room I was sharing with my father. I ran into the room and waited there.

Everything was quiet. I listened hard. And then I heard it.

Someone was coming up the stairs.

The footsteps were faint, but they were definitely coming up. It sounded like he had reached the second floor.

Then I heard a door opening, and the man's voice saying something, and the door closing. Then another door, and his voice, and the door closing. He must have been trying every door, looking for me in every room.

I was terrified. I knew he was almost finished searching that floor. And then what would he do?

Just as I thought. I heard him coming up the stairs. He reached the floor below me. Again, I heard him opening door after door. I could hear him more clearly now. He was saying things like "Where are you?" and "I know you're hiding here somewhere."

He finished searching the floor below me. And I heard him coming up.

I started crying, but silently, because I was so scared he would hear me. I sat all curled up in a corner, and I didn't know what to do. I didn't dare come out, because I knew he would hear my footsteps. I felt like a trapped animal. My eyes were darting around, looking for a place to hide...

He was on my floor now. I could hear his footsteps very clearly. And I heard his voice. It was like thunder.

"I know you're trying to run away from me," he boomed. "But I'm going to find you."

I don't think many kids have ever felt the kind of panic I felt then. I was alone in an empty, locked building with the scariest man I ever saw.

I looked around and saw a pile of blankets and old clothes on the floor.

Without stopping to think about it, I dove in, and covered myself with blankets.

I heard the door to the next room opening.

I heard the scary man's voice: "I know you're here, and I'm going to find you."

The door closed. I knew my turn had come.

The door to my room opened. His footsteps were very close. He stopped. I could feel him standing there, right by my hiding place.

Suddenly he yanked away the blankets, and caught me!

*   *   *

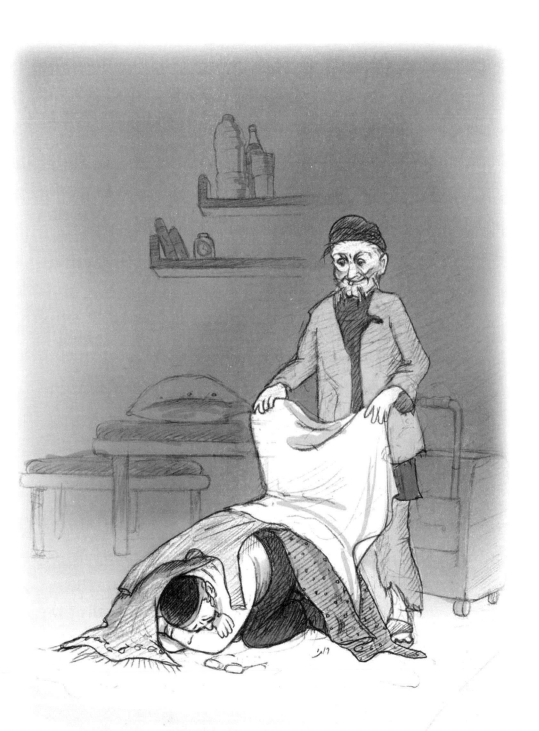

I looked at him in terror. I noticed he had a *yarmulke* on his head, but it was inside out, and he was wearing it at a strange angle.

There was no place to run to. I was paralyzed with fear. I couldn't even cry.

He looked at me and smiled, like a kid who just won a game.

"You see," he said. "You can't run away from me. I always find you in the end."

I didn't answer. I was afraid of what was going to happen next. I didn't know what he was going to do to me. Maybe hit me... maybe worse...

But he didn't. He started talking to me as if I were I his best friend.

"I'm good at hide-and-seek," he said. "No one can ever hide from me. I always find them."

The only words that came out of my mouth were, "The front door is locked. We're stuck in here."

He went to check. A few minutes later he came back and said, "You're right, it's locked. I'm going to call the police."

He went to the public phone at the end of the hall and called. I wanted to tell him that it was Rosh Hashanah and that he shouldn't use the phone, but I didn't have the nerve. I heard him giving them the address. When he hung up the phone, he told me that the police said they couldn't come now.

He talked for a few minutes about all sorts of things that had nothing to do with anything. Then he asked me if there were any clothes here that he could change into, and I told him there weren't. He said, "That's really chutzpah."

He went on talking and talking, mostly about himself, and then suddenly he walked over to the corner of the room, and started rummaging through a box that was sitting there. He found a pair of old pants and put them on over the ones he was wearing.

I started thinking that maybe he wasn't going to hurt me after all, but I was still scared.

Then he said, "Let's go and sit on the bench by the front door."

I went with him. I didn't know what else I could do. He talked and talked, and I prayed that someone would come and get me out of there.

Hashem answered my prayer. At that very moment, like something from a dream, my father appeared.

*　　*　　*

I didn't even hear him coming. Suddenly he was just there. When he saw me, he said, "Michoel, I've been waiting for you for..." Then he saw the strange man next to me and stopped.

"What are you doing here?" my father said to him.

"We've been playing hide-and-seek," said the man.

My father looked at me and saw the fear on my face. "Are you okay?" he asked me.

I nodded my head.

"Come with me," said my father.

We went out the front door, and the man yelled after us, "I won the game! I found him!"

My father asked me, "What happened in there, Michoel?"

I didn't answer him.

"Did that man hurt you?"

I shook my head.

"So what happened, then?"

I didn't answer.

I didn't talk for the whole two days of Rosh Hashanah. My father was very worried. I wanted to tell him, but the words just wouldn't come out of my mouth.

When we got home, my father told my mother about how I got locked in with the strange man. She tried to talk with me about it, but still the words just wouldn't come out of my mouth. That got my parents very worried.

Over the next few days I heard them talking to all sorts of people on the phone about me, trying to find out what they should do. Every time they finished talking with someone, they would come to me and say, "Tell us, Michoel. Are you sure that man didn't hurt you? He didn't hit you? He didn't touch you?"

No, no, no. I just kept shaking my head every time. He really hadn't done anything to me.

"Then why aren't you talking?" they asked.

I didn't answer, because I didn't know why. And besides, I just couldn't talk.

It went on like that for a week, and then another. I knew my parents were really getting very, very worried.

I don't know how to explain why I wasn't talking. I think something happened to me when I panicked for those few minutes on Rosh Hashanah when the man was after me, but I don't know exactly what. My parents kept using the word "trauma." I looked it up in the dictionary, and it said the word means shock, distress, and ordeal. Whoever wrote that dictionary knew just how I felt.

*　　　*　　　*

One day my father told me we were going to Bnei Brak to see a nice man — someone who talks to kids. I was glad, because I wanted to talk to someone, even though I wasn't managing to do it. I didn't know if I was going to say anything to him. I hoped I'd be able to talk.

When we got there, we went straight into his office. He was sitting in a big chair, and had a computer on a desk. He said I should sit in the chair facing him.

I sat down.

He looked at me and didn't say anything. I looked back at him and didn't say anything.

Then he said, "I heard about what happened to you, and I can't make up my mind if it was very scary, or very funny."

That question bothered me. *What does he mean by "funny"?* I said to myself. It wasn't funny at all.

To tell you the truth, his question made me mad. For this I came all the way from Modiin Illit to Bnei Brak, to have this guy ask me if the terrible time I had was funny?

"What's funny about it?" I heard myself say angrily. "There's nothing funny about it."

I was talking!

"Oh," he said. "Well, maybe I didn't hear the story

exactly right, because the story I heard sounded pretty scary, but it was funny at the same time."

"Then I guess you didn't hear what really happened."

"Maybe you'd better tell me, then," he suggested, "so I'll get it straight. If you'll let me, I'll type what you tell me into my computer."

I decided to tell him.

I talked, and he listened and typed what I said. When I was finished, he printed out what he'd typed and gave it to me, and asked me to read it out loud. This is what it said:

Question: Tell me, what happened?

Answer: I got up at about eight-thirty. I got ready for *shul*, and I tried to leave the building. But the front door was locked. I started looking in all the rooms for someone, but there wasn't anyone in the whole building. Then a man who was sort of bad came and started looking for me. I ran for my life. I went into my room and hid under some blankets and clothes. He came looking for me. He looked in every room. After about half an hour, he found me hiding there under the blankets. He had a *yarmulke*, but he didn't even know how to wear it right. He started talking to me, and I started to feel a little less scared. I could see that he was "koo-koo" (crazy). I told him the front door was locked. He went to check, and all of a sudden he went to the phone and called the police. I was too scared to tell him phone calls aren't allowed on Rosh Hashanah. He told the police what street we were on. Then he hung up, and he told me the police said they couldn't come now. He asked me if there were any clothes here for him, so he could change, and I said there weren't any. Then he said, "That's really chutzpah." There was a box full of old clothes there, and he started looking through it. Finally he found a pair of pants and put them on over the ones he was wearing. I noticed that he put them on backwards...

(The man, laughing): I guess you didn't tell him to put them on the right away...

(Me, laughing): Oh, no! That was all I needed...

Question: What did you do after that?

Answer: We sat down on a bench, and he talked to me.

Question: What did he talk about?

Answer: I don't remember.

Question: And how did the story end?

Answer: My father came and opened the door. He said he thought I must have gone to another *shul*, so he didn't come looking for me until then. My father noticed that I wasn't answering him, and he went and called the man who was in charge of the dormitory and told him he shouldn't have let the scary man in.

After I finished reading it, he asked, "When you think about this story, is it funny or scary?"

"Scary."

"What scares you?"

"I feel like I'm there right now."

"Hmm... did anything bad actually happen to you there?"

"Not really. I was just scared."

"Scared of what?"

"The man looked very scary."

"Were you scared of the way he looked, or of what you thought he was going do to you?"

"At first, I thought he was going to hit me, but he didn't hit me... so then I was just scared of the way he looked."

He looked at me, thought for a minute, and then said, "Michoel, this really is a scary story, but there are also some funny parts to it, aren't there?"

"Do you mean the part where he put the pants on backwards?" I asked.

"Yes," he answered. "I mean, I can just picture it. A kid is sitting there, scared to death, and this crazy fellow, this 'koo-koo,' as you call him, starts putting on a pair of pants backwards. Didn't you feel like laughing?"

"I wasn't exactly in the mood to laugh," I said.

"I understand that," he said. "But now, when you look back at it, some of it sounds pretty funny, doesn't it?"

"I guess so," I said. "But I was really scared at the time."

Then the man said, "Let's work on this story and change it from scary to funny."

"Change it?" I said. I didn't see how we could change something that already happened.

"That's right. We're going to change it from a scary story to a funny story, with you as the hero."

I still didn't see how we were supposed to do that. If I was scared, I was scared. How could we change it?

"What have you got there on your computer?" I said. "Some kind of magic button that changes things that happened to people?"

He laughed. "No, I haven't got any kind of magic

button. Let me show you how it's done."

He asked me to tell the story again.

I told him everything I just told you, but he kept making me go into all the details, starting from the first time I met the strange man right before Rosh Hashanah, when I was with my friends, and how the man almost caught me, but I ran away.

I told him about my bad dreams on Rosh Hashanah night, and how I got up late the next morning. Then I got to the part about finding myself trapped in the dormitory building. He kept asking me how I felt every moment. He was excited that I had the courage to try to escape from the man. He kept saying it was great that I didn't give up.

Then we came to the part where the man found me and began talking with me. When I told it over a second time, I could see it was kind of funny.

"Think of it," he said. "The scariest man in the world is standing there with a pair of pants on backwards over his own pants, and he's talking to you as if you were his best friend. He doesn't even notice how terrified you are of him; he just keeps on talking and, at the same time, he's trying to close his backwards pants..."

I had to admit, it was funny, especially the way he described it. Pretty soon we were rolling with laughter at the scary story that happened to me.

I saw that the story really had changed — at least a little bit.

When we stopped laughing, we were both quiet for a moment. Then he said, "Michoel, I'm not trying to convince you that what happened to you was fun. I know that if you had your choice, you wouldn't have wanted this to happen to you. But now that it already happened, we might as well try to get something good out of it."

"Something good?"

"Yeah. You're a hero. You have courage. You didn't just stand there and cry, you took action. That shows how very brave you are. Did you know all this about yourself before this story happened?"

I didn't know what to say.

"I think that now you can be much more sure of yourself than you used to be," he continued, "because you went through a tough experience, and nothing happened to you. That makes you different from a kid who never had to deal with such a situation."

I thought for a moment. I realized that he was right, but I still felt kind of scared.

"Okay," I said. "But how do I get rid of the scary feelings I still have?"

"You should go and see that man."

"Go and see him?"

"Yes, I really mean it. This man you met is actually a poor, harmless fellow, who happens to have a mind that doesn't work very well, and he also happens to be scary-looking. In your imagination, you have a picture of him as a dangerous man, but he isn't really dangerous. In order to get rid of this scary picture, the best thing to do is to see him again, and this time, see him the way he really is. The reality will chase away the scary picture that you have in your imagination."

That was the end of the meeting. He gave me a printout of the story I told him. Then my father and I went home.

On the way home, I showed the printout to my father. When we got home I showed it to my mother and to my younger brothers and sisters, too. And the next day, when I went to school, I showed it to all my friends. I felt different about the story, now that I'd talked about it. I felt much better.

But I wasn't finished "changing the story" yet.

*   *   *

The next week, my father took me to Jerusalem. We went to the place where the scary man lived.

We didn't go inside; my father asked someone to go and call the man. I felt scared inside, but I knew this was what I had to do.

The man came out. He came over to us. I saw that his face wasn't as scary as I'd thought. At first he didn't know who we were or why we were bothering him, but then he remembered me.

"Oh, here's my friend," he said.

I looked at him.

"We *davened* together on Rosh Hashanah," said the man.

Sure we did, I said to myself. But I just smiled at him.

"Thank you for the trousers," he said.

This time I couldn't help laughing. He thought I gave him the pants as a present!

"They fit me perfectly," he said.

He really wasn't scary after all. He was just a poor, good-hearted guy who was kind of "koo-koo."

My father handed me a package. It was a present we'd bought for the man, a sweater. I gave it to him.

"Oh, thank you!" he said.

"You're welcome," I answered.

"All right, are you ready to go now?" my father asked.

I nodded. We said goodbye to the man and started walking away.

"Hey, the sweater even matches the trousers!" he called out after us.

We laughed.

We went home to Modiin Illit, knowing that now the story had "changed." It was another story now, not scary anymore, because I told it over again and looked at it in a different way.

*   *   *

I called up that nice man who talks to kids and told him what happened. He promised me that my story would be in the next volume of *Kids Speak*, to help other kids who have been through traumas. He said they could learn from me how to tell a story over again and change it into something good. He said he would let me choose a title if I wanted. First I thought of calling it "Changing the Story," but then I thought of a better title. I decided to call it "That's Another Story."

You must be wondering how he could promise me that my story would be in *Kids Speak*.

So I'll tell you who he is. He is the author of all the *Kids Speak* books!

Glossary

The following glossary provides a partial explanation of some of the Hebrew and Yiddish (Y.) words and phrases used in this book. The spellings and explanations reflect the way the specific word is used herein. Often, there are alternate spellings and meanings for the words.

ABBA: Daddy.

AVEIRAH: sin.

BARUCH HASHEM: thank G-d.

BEIS HAMIKDASH: the Holy Temple at Jerusalem.

BEIS MEDRASH: house of study; a post high-school learning program.

CHAS V'SHALOM: G-d forbid.

CHEREM: a ban.

CHESHBON NEFESH: a spiritual accounting.

CHUMASH: the Bible.

DAVENED (Y): prayed.

HALACHAH: Jewish law.

HAMELECH: literally, "the King"; a prayer recited on Rosh Hashanah.

HASHEM: G-d.

HATZOLAH: volunteer emergency ambulance service.

HECHSHER: kosher certification.

IMA: Mommy.

KAPARAH: an atonement.

MAKKAS KINIM: plague of lice.

MASECHES KIDDUSHIN: Tractate of *Kiddushin.*

MECHILAH: forgiveness.

MIDDAH (PL. MIDDOS): character trait(s).

MINCHAH: afternoon prayers.

MISHLEI: the Book of Proverbs.

MISHNAYOS: a set of volumes of the Mishnah.

NEIGEL VASSER (Y.): literally, "nail water"; washing one's hands after waking up to remove spiritual impurity.

RAV: rabbi.

ROSH CHODESH: the beginning of the Jewish month.

SEFARIM: books; holy books.

SHIUR: a class; a lesson.

SHUL: synagogue.

SIMCHAH: happiness; a joyous occasion.

TALMIDIM: students.

TALMUD TORAH: a Jewish elementary school for boys.

TEHILLIM: the Book of Psalms.

TESHUVAH: repentance.

TOOSHIYAH: resourcefulness.

TZADDEIKES: a pious, righteous girl or woman.

TZADDIKIM: pious, righteous men.

YARMULKE (Y.): skullcap; a head covering worn by Jewish boys and men.

YOM TOV (PL. YAMIM TOVIM): Jewish holy day(s).